# Dawson's Creek

## The Official Scrapbook

BASED ON THE TELEVISION SHOW
*DAWSON'S CREEK*
CREATED BY KEVIN WILLIAMSON

BY K.S. RODRIGUEZ

EBURY PRESS • LONDON

First published 1998 by Pocket Books, New York, USA

1 3 5 7 6 10 8 6 4 2

© 1998 Columbia TriStar Television, Inc.

First published in UK in 1998 by Ebury Press
Random House, 20 Vauxhall Bridge Road, London SW1V 2SA

Random House Australia Pty Limited
20 Alfred Street, Milsons Point, Sydney, New South Wales 2061, Australia

Random House New Zealand Limited
18 Poland Road, Glenfield, Auckland 10, New Zealand

Random House South Africa (Pty) Limited
Endulini, 5A Jubilee Road, Parktown 2193, South Africa

Random House UK Limited Reg. No. 954009

A CIP catalogue record for this book is available from the British Library

ISBN 0091867878

Interior book design by Mark Pessoni

Front and back photographs copyright 1998 © by Columbia TriStar Television, Inc.

Childhood photographs of Joshua Jackson on pages 22 and 23 copyright and courtesy of Joshua Jackson

Printed and bound in France by Pollina – n° 75785

Papers used by Ebury Press are natural, recyclable products made from wood grown in sustainable forests.

# SOMETIMES BEING A WRITER CAN GET YOU INTO TROUBLE.

For example, imagine writing about something completely autobiographical like *Dawson's Creek*. Then imagine actually *admitting* that it's autobiographical. Your friends laugh at you. Critics pulverize you. And your mom and dad just want to know how come they never knew about your unconditional love for Katie Couric.

It's certainly no secret that I borrow a lot of my own personal history when I write. For example, *Dawson's Creek* is a little inlet of water near a bridge just about five miles from where I grew up. Joey is based on my high school sweetheart, Fanny Norwood. She's the one I pined for, secretly, and agonizingly watched as she dated all the hot high school studs. Fortunately, when they finally broke her heart (which they always did) I was there to help her pick up the pieces.

Dawson Leery's love for Spielberg definitely doesn't come out of nowhere. I believe Spielberg to be god and the primary influence in my professional life. I read once that he made home movies in his backyard, so I found an old 8mm camera that my parents had packed away and shot my own home movies. My first, WHITE AS A GHOST, included a cherry Jell-O decapitation sequence complete with spaghetti noodles.

*Dawson's Creek* is my true love. It combines all the memories of my childhood (and a lot of memories the writers and I created to make it more exciting—because *nobody's* life is that exciting) with the kind of storytelling that I always hope to be a part of. Part real, part Hollywood fantasy. My work is both. My goal is to take smart and articulate characters who can comment, poke fun, agonize, be surprised, laugh at themselves, self-referentiate, but ultimately react very honestly and humanly to what's happening around them.

Of course, this show isn't all my doing—not even close. There is a huge group of incredibly talented, dedicated people that bring this show to life week after week. The cast: James, Josh, Michelle, Katie, John, Mary-Margaret, Nina, and Mary Beth. They are all wonderfully gifted actors and delightful human beings. And the writing team, who have managed to take my dream and turn it into such a tremendous reality. The show is theirs. And the joyous and fearless leader everyone has in Paul Stupin, the other Executive Producer and my co-conspirator/partner in crime. Without this group, *Dawson's Creek* would not be. (And it doesn't hurt to be involved with the heroes at Columbia/TriStar TV and the WB Network, either.)

We couldn't be more thrilled that *Dawson's Creek* has reached its audience with the kind of emotional force that we only ever dreamed about. Kids, fathers, boyfriends, college students, grandmothers, high school freshmen—everyone has tuned in week after week to experience the world of Dawson, Joey, Paccy, and Jen. To laugh with them or cry with them. To share in the stories that they live through. To know them, as we all do. And we plan to continue their journey for as long as we can, because it would be a shame to miss out on any of it.

*Kevin Williamson*

It has the perfect mix for must-watch television: juicy plots, romantic tension, quick-as-a-whip dialogue, and smart, articulate, authentic characters. The high-quality scripts combined with skilled acting and the magic of a small, charming town make *Dawson's Creek* unique.   But there are four other elements that have fans absolutely wild over the show:  James Van Der Beek (Dawson), Katie Holmes (Joey), Joshua Jackson (Pacey), and Michelle Williams (Jen).  These young talents perfectly capture teenage passion, insecurity, and angst to turn out genuine performances that have been wowing critics and fans the world over.

What are James, Josh, Katie, and Michelle really like?  What did these young actors do before they landed in Capeside?  Which star is most like his or her character? Who likes to dance in the makeup trailer?  Which actor brings a dog to the set each day?  And what other projects can fans look forward to seeing them in?   Turn the page and find out . . . .

Did you know? On the set, the actors sit in chairs with their characters' names on them—not their own names— to lessen the likelihood of fans stealing the canvas backs.

# DAWSON LEERY

Dawson Leery, age fifteen, is the only child of Mitch and Gale Leery. His life revolves around film: he takes a film class at Capeside High; he and best pal, Joey, spend every Friday night—"movie night"—watching movie after movie; he works part-time in Capeside's video store; and he spends most of his spare time making his own films. His dream is to follow in the footsteps of his idol, filmmaker Steven Spielberg.

Because of his avid interest in film, Dawson is a dreamer and tends to romanticize life. He wishes his life were more like the movies, but he does have two feet on the ground. Dawson is smart and sensitive, an attentive boyfriend who likes to surprise his girl with sweet romantic gestures, and a good friend who's always there to lend a sympathetic ear.

Though he fell for Jen Lindley when she first came to town, his feelings for his best friend, Joey Potter, have been heating up. Dawson finds himself caught in a confusing love triangle that allures and scares him at the same time.

As a child, Dawson was short and pudgy, which earned him the nickname "Oompa-Loompa," after the diminutive people in *Willy Wonka and the Chocolate Factory*. But in his teens, he has far outgrown his nickname by emerging into a tall, slender, handsome, clean-cut teenager with the makings of an out-and-out heartthrob. Just ask Joey . . . .

"I believe that all the mysteries of the universe, all the answers to all life's questions, can be found in a Spielberg film. It's a theory I've been working on. See, whenever I have a problem, all I have to do is look to the right Spielberg movie and the answer is revealed."—Dawson Leery

**Did you know?** After several unsuccessful attempts at molding a latex "Joey" face for Dawson's famous mask-kissing scene, the props people came up with something else. The "rubber" Joey mask on which Dawson practiced his kissing technique was actually concrete—and weighed about 30 pounds!

# JAMES VAN DER BEEK

James Van Der Beek, the oldest of three children, was born in Cheshire, Connecticut. He was bitten by the acting bug literally by accident, after a concussion at age thirteen landed him off the football field and into the theater as Danny Zuko in *Grease*. When James' parents saw the talent their son had, they allowed him to start auditioning for jobs in New York City at the age of sixteen.

Before long, he won roles in an off-Broadway play, Edward Albee's *Finding the Sun* and in *Shenandoah* at the Goodspeed Opera House in Connecticut. He snagged his first film role soon after, as an arrogant jock in *Angus*—a far cry from sensitive Dawson.

James claims he is like Dawson: "He's a lot like I was at fifteen—innocent, idealistic, impassioned, and often clueless." He thinks viewers relate to Dawson because he is "the dork in all of us."

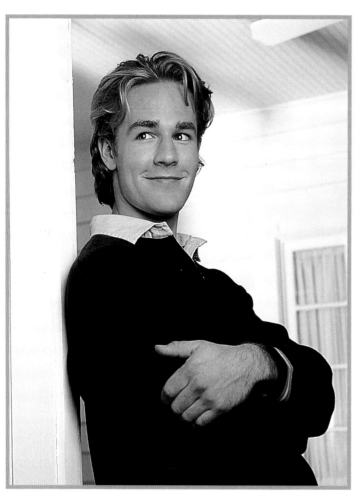

But James was no Oompa-Loompa as a kid. He earned the nickname "Beek" on the football team, stemming from his Dutch last name, which means "by the brook." But the nickname that stuck was "Baby James," which cast members in a play called him to distinguish him from four older Jameses in the production.

After winning a scholarship to Drew University, James put his career on hold for his education. He enjoyed studying English and Sociology at the Madison, New Jersey, school, but he soon missed being on stage and in front of the camera. Restless, he searched out more work and came upon the lead role in *Dawson's Creek*. The script impressed him: he wanted that role.

Meanwhile, the producers of *Dawson's Creek* felt they had exhausted their search, and as time was coming close for the series to be filmed, they didn't know if they'd ever find the right lead. But James's audition tape caught the attention of the casting

Full name:  James William Van Der Beek
Nickname:  Baby James, Beek
Birth Date:  March 8, 1977
Star Sign: Pisces
Birthplace: Cheshire, Connecticut
Siblings:  One younger brother and one younger sister
Hobbies:  Sports, reading, writing, shooting pool
Favorite Color:  Blue

directors, and it was immediately FedExed to producer Paul Stupin's home. Stupin watched the tape and sighed with relief: he had finally found Dawson. Three days later, James was notified that he had won the role. James certainly left an impression, his audition tape became stuck in Stupin's VCR. It is still stuck there to this day.

James plans to return to school eventually, but right now he is riding a rocket to superstardom with the busy *Dawson's Creek* filming schedule and two movies ready for release: he costars in *I Love You. . . I Love You Not* with teen sensation Claire Danes, and in an independent film, *Harvest.*

When James is off-screen, he enjoys boating with *Dawson's Creek's* cast and crew, reading favorite books such as James Joyce's *Portrait of the Artist as a Young Man*, writing, and playing sports.

Did you know? It takes seven full days of shooting to make one episode of *Dawson's Creek*.

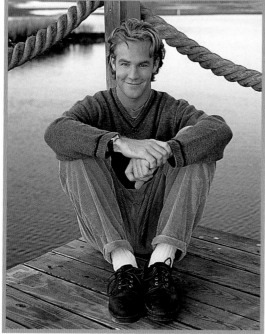

# JENNIFER LINDLEY

This new girl in town turned many heads in Capeside when she arrived, especially Dawson Leery's. Jen arrived in town just in time to start her sophomore year at Capeside High School. Her parents sent her to live in the small town ostensibly to help care for her ill grandfather but really to get away from the big-city temptations, bad influences, and ex-boyfriends that New York City had to offer. Instead of life in the fast lane, she has taken a few steps back to grow up in quiet Capeside—and in the process even learned a thing or two.

Grappling with religious Grams isn't easy for Jen, and experiencing her grandfather's slow death was harder than she ever imagined. And even though not everyone in Capeside was as friendly as Dawson and Cliff Elliot, she eventually found her niche, and a friend in her chief rival, Joey Potter.

Jen is mature, thoughtful, self-confident, intellectual, and sophisticated without being snobby, and she just wants to lead the life of a normal teenage girl. Despite her past, she seems to have her head on straight, but she does experience moments of uncertainty and insecurity, though she tries her best not to let it show.

"You know, I really am a cliché, Dawson. In New York I was moving fast. I was moving really, really fast. I kept stumbling and falling. But here I feel like for the first time in a long time, I'm walking at a steady pace. And I'm afraid that if I kiss you my knees may buckle, I may stumble, and I don't think I could deal with that right now."—Jen Lindley

**Did you know?** Unlike Jen and Joey, Michelle and Katie instantly bonded in real life.

# MICHELLE WILLIAMS

orn in Kalispell, Montana, Michelle Williams made a change from small town life to the big city when her family moved to San Diego when she was ten years old—just the opposite of her character, Jen Lindley. In San Diego, Michelle became involved in community theater and then started to commute to Los Angeles to audition for television and movie roles. She soon won guest appearances on television shows such as *Step by Step* and *Home Improvement*, then landed her first feature film role at the age of fourteen in *Lassie*, followed quickly by the role of an alien in the sci-fi cult hit *Species*. When more parts started to come in, Michelle accelerated her high school classes, graduated early at the age of 16, and continued to work in film. One of her

greatest learning experiences was acting beside movie greats Jessica Lange, Jennifer Jason Leigh, and Michelle Pfeiffer in *A Thousand Acres*.

When Michelle auditioned for the role of Jen, the producers thought she brought the perfect blend of maturity, rebelliousness, and vulnerability to the role with her great acting and stunning good looks. Michelle is mature and introspective like Jen, and she can relate to Jen's plight of feeling like an outsider in Capeside: Michelle told one teen magazine that she spent most of her time in high school hiding in the bathroom stalls from bullies.

In her free time, Michelle is a voracious reader who enjoys watching 1980s teen flicks with Katie Holmes and keeping fit by running and boxing. Fans can look forward to seeing Michelle in the films *Halloween H20*, starring Jamie Lee Curtis and written by Kevin Williamson, and *Dick*, with Kirsten Dunst, about two girls who get lost on a White House tour and meet President Richard Nixon.

**Did you know?** Michelle's girlhood dream was to become the first female heavyweight champion of the world.

| | | | |
|---|---|---|---|
| Full Name: | Michelle Williams | Birthplace: | Kalispell, Montana |
| Nickname: | None | Siblings: | Four |
| Birth Date: | September 9, 1980 | Hobbies: | Reading, boxing |
| Star Sign: | Virgo | | |

# PACEY WITTER

Trouble. Incompetent. An embarrassment. That's how Pacey Witter's intolerant family would characterize him. But his best friends would call him sensitive, independent, eager, insecure, witty, and disarmingly charming. Pacey is the youngest in his hard-core family of three older sisters and one older brother. His father is Capeside's sheriff, putting a lot of pressure on him to behave, not to mention his brother, Doug, dutiful deputy to Dad and chronic Pacey-harasser. Like Joey, he uses his sense of humor and sharp wit as a guard to his sensitive soul: deep down, Pacey wants to be liked and accepted. And though it may not seem like it at first, Pacey does try to do the right thing.

Pacey has had bad luck with girls his age, which might explain why he was drawn to his English teacher, Tamara Jacobs. His brief time with her taught him a lot of painful but valuable lessons, and he surprisingly handled the scandal and breakup with the grace of a mature man.

An underachiever, he's not a student, though he is smart. Pacey doesn't see why he should rise above everyone's (low) expectations of him. Though he's not a jock, he enjoys sports, especially basketball. He earns extra money by working at Screenplay Video with his best buddy, Dawson. There's never a dull moment with Pacey, whether it is because of his offbeat sense of humor or his unabashed antics, like "borrowing" his father's car or entering a beauty pageant.

"You know what Dawson? I don't know how to tell you this—but the guy with the brown hair and the throbbing neck muscles . . . the guy with Tamara Jacobs . . . that's . . . that's . . . me."—Pacey Witter

**Did you know?** In the "Detention" episode Pacey (the character) refers to *The Mighty Ducks* movies that Josh (the actor) starred in.

# JOSHUA "JOSH" JACKSON

Though he's only in his early twenties, Josh Jackson already had a truckload of acting experience behind him when he joined the cast of *Dawson's Creek*. His career started in his hometown of Vancouver, Canada, where he appeared in television ads promoting tourism in British Columbia. By the age of eleven he had already won a role in a feature film, *Crooked Hearts*, and soon thereafter landed the lead in the Seattle production of *Willy Wonka and the Chocolate Factory*. His biggest break came with the Disney hit *The Mighty Ducks*, which went on to have two sequels in which Josh co-starred. Other movie parts quickly followed, in *Andre the Seal*, *Digger*, and *Magic in the Water*. Joshua also starred in two Showtime films, *Robin of Locksley* and *Ronnie and Julie*.

When the producers of *Dawson's Creek* saw Josh's audition for Pacey, they knew

they had found their man. They felt that Josh perfectly captured Pacey's sly attitude. Soon they found out that was for a reason—cast and crew agree that Josh is most like his character. "Like Pacey, I also have an offbeat sense of humor and I enjoy laughing, having a good time, and often get myself in trouble for it. But neither of us is mischievous for mischief's sake. Pacey's in his own world, doing his own thing, which unfortunately seems to offend a lot of people." Despite the similarities, Josh seems to be slightly more serious than Pacey: though he's the clown on the set, Josh also enjoys reading philosophy.

Off the set, Josh enjoys spending time with the cast and crew of *Dawson's Creek*, who in turn say he is "fun to hang with," and his constant companion, Shumba, a large Rhodesian Ridgeback, who loyally comes to work with Josh every day.

Fans can look forward to seeing Josh in more feature films, including *Apt Pupil*, a film based on a Stephen King short story in which he co-stars with Brad Renfro, and *Urban Legend*, a spin on the horror film genre, co-starring with Jared Leto and Alicia Witt, and *Cruel Inventions*, a modern version of *Dangerous Liaisons*, set in an affluent prep school, starring Ryan Phillipe and Sarah Michelle Geller.

Full Name: Joshua Jackson
Nickname: Josh, Jackson
Birth Date: June 11, 1978
Star Sign: Gemini
Birthplace: Vancouver, British Columbia
Favorite Color: Brown
Pets: Shumba, a Rhodesian Ridgeback
Siblings: One younger sister
Hobbies: Reading, sports

Left, above, and right: Cute from the start! Josh's own family photos capture his star personality.

Did you know? The dog in the J. Crew catalog that features the cast of *Dawson's Creek* is Josh's very own pet, Shumba.

There's more than meets the eye to this fifteen-year-old girl next door—or rather, girl across the creek. Tomboy Josephine "Joey" Potter has had to grow up quickly, learning the hard way to be self-reliant. Having lost her mother to cancer, and with her father in prison, Joey lives with her older sister, Bessie, and Bessie's infant son, Alexander. Joey and her makeshift family struggle but are able to make ends meet through the S. S. Icehouse, the touristy restaurant Bessie runs, where Joey waits on tables. Though Joey's family situation fuels small–town gossip in Capeside, Joey is able to rise above it all and wade through her difficult teenage years with hopes of getting a college scholarship.

Joey comes across as tough and self-assured, with a sharp tongue and intelligence, but inside she's insecure about her budding beauty and sexuality. Her feelings about best pal Dawson have especially confused her: they quickly changed from companionship to longing. When Jen Lindley comes into the picture and steals Dawson's heart, these feelings plague Joey even more, and she eventually gets what she wants. Things start to ignite between her and Dawson, leaving her utterly bewildered. Joey wonders if their relationship can stand the heat. . . .

"I just think our emerging hormones are destined to alter our relationship and I'm trying to limit the fallout."—Joey Potter

# KATIE HOLMES

Katie Holmes was born in Toledo, Ohio, the youngest of five children. Though Katie had Tinseltown aspirations, she never thought she'd be able to break out of her small-town life and burst onto the entertainment scene so quickly.

In Toledo, Katie studied at a modeling school and acted in high school productions. When an agent spotted her at a modeling convention and encouraged her to come to Los Angeles, she nervously accepted the offer. She found herself at her first professional audition ever, for the critically acclaimed and award winning film, *The Ice Storm*, starring Kevin Kline and Sigourney Weaver. Katie's sparkling talent won her the role in an instant.

That gave Katie the courage to audition for *Dawson's Creek*. Her mother taped her audition in the basement of their house. Producers of *Dawson's Creek* didn't care much about the quality of Katie's tape, but they did care a great deal about Katie's acting talent. They immediately knew they had found their Joey in sweet, small-town girl Katie Holmes.

When *Dawson's Creek* producers contacted Katie for a callback, she had a major problem: they wanted her to come out to Los Angeles just when she was set to star in her high school production of *Damn Yankees*.

Rather than back out on her responsibility to her school, Katie asked the producers to postpone her callback until after the musical ended its run.

Co–stars and producers can't believe that sweet, beautiful, naive Katie is playing a tomboy with an acid tongue. And unlike Joey, she's isn't very good at rowing a boat—the boat is actually towed by an underwater rope. But Katie does think she has a few things in common with her character. She told *Us* magazine, "I'm actually working on becoming more like my character. She's so smart and strong. And witty."

Katie's fans have a lot to look forward to in the next couple of years in addition to *Dawson's Creek*. Her film projects include *Disturbing Behavior*, in which she plays a character a lot less wholesome than Joey Potter; *Killing Mrs. Tingle*, another Kevin Williamson vehicle; and *Go*, in which she stars with *Party of Five* heartthrob Scott Wolf.

Full Name: Katherine Holmes
Nickname: Katie
Birth Date: December 18, 1978
Star Sign: Sagittarius
Birthplace: Toledo, Ohio
Siblings: Three older sisters and one older brother
Hobbies: Dancing and shopping

# LOCATION, LOCATION, LOCATION

The interior of Dawson's room is a studio set, but the exterior of the Leery house is a private home near Hewletts Creek, North Carolina.

Though Capeside is supposed to be a waterside hamlet in New England, it is in reality a picturesque seaside town in Wilmington, North Carolina.

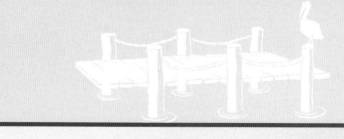

When Dawson and Pacey aren't in school, they earn extra cash at Screenplay Video. The interior of Capeside High is shot in an old studio that was used for the show *Matlock*. Exterior scenes are filmed at the University of North Carolina at Wilmington.

Being a native of North Carolina, creator-producer-writer Kevin Williamson chose the state for the settings of both *I Know What You Did Last Summer* and *Dawson's Creek*. He loves the beauty and the familiarity of the area. Wilmington has a big screen and small screen history, having been the backdrop for films such as *Firestarter*, *To Gillian on Her 37th Birthday*, *The Hudsucker Proxy*, *Lolita* and *Billy Bathgate* and for television shows such as *American Gothic* and *Matlock*.

Michelle, James, Katie, and Josh relax between takes. The stars are friends off the set, too. At one point, Josh and James shared an apartment in Wilmington, and the four of them enjoy hanging with the crew at Vinnie's and the Deluxe, their favorite local eateries.

# SCENES WE'D LIKE TO SEE AGAIN. . . AND AGAIN

New Girl in Town: There's a new girl in Capeside, and while Pacey and Dawson are eager to meet and greet . . .

. . . Joey is a little less enthusiastic . . .

. . . especially when Jen is chosen to star with her in Dawson's movie.

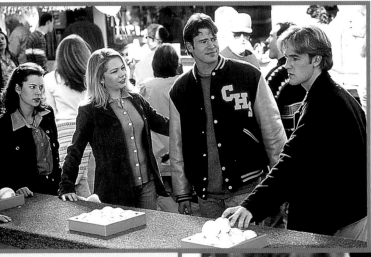

While Dawson and Cliff vie for Jen's attention, Mary Beth hopes Cliff will broaden his horizons and notice her.

Who can blame both girls if they choose their stuffed animals over the boys and their puffed-up egos?

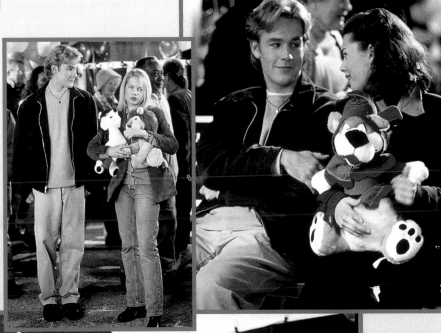

**Pageantry:** The Miss Windjammer Contest brought many things to light:

. . . Joey can sing, Pacey looks smashing in a tuxedo (and should have won the contest) . . .

. . . and when Dawson stops looking through the camera and starts looking at real life, he finally realizes that his best friend Joey is a babe!

**A Kiss Is Just a Kiss——or Is It?:** The beginning of the end for Dawson and Jen signals a new beginning for best buddies Dawson and Joey. Dawson and Joey strive to answer the question: can best friends be lovers?

# STYLES OF THE STARS

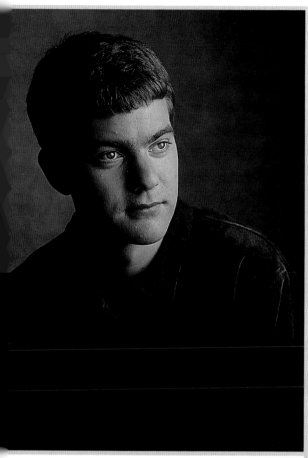

The look in Capeside is casual cool, and each character has a unique style that signals exactly who he or she is. Joey's sexy-casual halter and shorts accentuate her tomboy femininity. Dawson is comfortable in a T-shirt and baggy shorts. His pendant makes an earthy and offbeat statement.

Individualist Pacey sports a retro-cool style, shown in his penchant for bowling shirts. Jen easily makes the transition from urban chic to Capeside comfort in this breezy floral dress. Her flip-do brings out the voguish city girl at heart.

Joey's classic straight locks extend her simple charm, whether she wears her hair loose, or up in a twist. Even though Joey characterizes Pacey as "a D student with a Julius Caesar haircut," he's right in style. Dawson's locks are more poetic, a nice loose contrast to his usual neat flannel shirts and khakis.

There's nothing mismatched about Dawson and Joey.

CONTINUED:

                    JOEY
We're fifteen, we start high school on
Monday....and I have breasts.

                    DAWSON
~~WHAT?~~ Uh-huh-uh What?

                    JOEY
And you have genitalia.

                    DAWSON
I've always had genitalia.

                    JOEY
But there's more of it.

                    DAWSON
How do you know?

                    JOEY
        (matter of fact)
Long fingers--gotta go.  Seeya.

Joey starts to crawl out the window.

                    DAWSON
Whoah Joe.  Don't hit and run, explain
yourself.

                    JOEY
We're not kids anymore.  It's time to
evolvvvvve.

                    DAWSON
Wait a second.  Has something happened
you're not telling me?

                    JOEY
~~Nothing notable.~~  I just think our
emerging hormones are destined to alter
our relationship ~~and I'm trying to limit
the fallout.~~

                    DAWSON
~~What fallout?  Are you saying we can't be
friends anymore?~~

                    JOEY
~~I'm saying we're changing~~ and we have to
adjust or the male-female thing will get
in the way.

These two teleplay pages from the pilot episode show hand-written comments and changes from creator-writer-producer Kevin Williamson. His knack for writing smart teen dialogue makes *Dawson's Creek* distinctive. The actors often say that his lines roll off the tongue, making their acting job easy.

                                        (CONTINUED)

CONTINUED:

                    JEN
          Well...that depends on a lot of things.
          Gramps' heart condition, my mom and
          dad...

Jen, eyeing Joey, changes the subject.

                    JEN
          I love your lipstick.  What shade is
          that?

Dawson takes note.  Joey is stung with embarrassment.  She
rebounds instantly.

                    JOEY
          Wicked red.  Look, guys, let's just jump
          to the chase here 'cause this sweaty palm
          foreplay is getting old real quick.  Jen,
          are you a virgin?

*I like guys hair colors, what # is that? Return w/ that line*

Jen chokes on air.  Dawson's mouth drops.

                    DAWSON
          That's mature.

                    JOEY
          Because Dawson is a virgin and two
          virgins really makes for a clumsy first
          encounter.  Don't you think?

                    DAWSON
          You are gonna die.  Painfully.

                    JOEY
          I'm just trying to escalate the process.
          Some of us are falling asleep here.

                    JEN
          It's okay, Dawson.  Yes, I'm a virgin.
          How about you Joey, are you?

She smiles, challenging Joey.

*go inside. See something that fires up Joey. Comes out of nowhere.*

                    JOEY
          Please.  Years ago.  Trucker named Bubba.

Jen is making a genuine effort.  Dawson leans into Joey's
ear.

*born out Joey*

                    DAWSON
          What is up with you?

Joey shrugs as they move to the ticket window.

# DID YOU KNOW?

**Did you know?** James' father pitched for the Los Angeles Dodgers.

**Did you know?** Because school was in session during the filming of the "Detention" episode and the producers wanted to use the local high school library, the episode had to be filmed after school hours, from 5:00 P.M. until about 5:00 A.M.

**Did you know?** Katie had to sit still for about two hours—three different times—while rubber was poured on her face to make the "Joey mask" on which Dawson practices his kissing.

**Did you know?** Josh once sang with the San Francisco Boys Chorus.

**Did you know?** Katie has been accepted at Columbia University, an Ivy League school in New York City. She has deferred admission.

**Did you know?** Josh received two marriage proposals from Japanese fans after *The Mighty Ducks* movies came out.

**Did you know?** The worst thing about filming by the creek is the bugs!

**Did you know?** *Dawson's Creek* is becoming the most talked about show on the air. It is also the WB network's highest rated show ever.

"A thang? No, I'm not getting a thang for you, Dawson. I've known you too long. I've seen you burp, barf, pick your nose, scratch your butt. I don't think I'm getting a thang for you."—Joey

Jen: Hey Joey, I love your lipstick. Wha[t] shade is that?
Joey: Wicked red. I love your hair color[.] What number is that?

Pacey: Come on, Jen. I mean, it's pretty obvious that you're missing the undivided attention of our friend Dawson. Maybe feeling a little dumper's remorse?
Jen: You're way off.
Pacey: Tell me, is it the possibility of losing him to somebody that suddenly makes him seem attractive?
Jen: You really think I'm that shallow, huh?
Pacey: No, I think you're that human.

Joey: No time to talk, Dawson. My sister's having her baby.
Dawson: Cool. Congratulations.
Joey: On your lawn.

"That's right. I'm done trying to turn my life into some exciting movie because you know what? I'll only end up getting disappointed. Like when I started seeing Jen—I thought, okay, you know what—from now on everything is gonna be some big epic romance—you know, tortured and passionate and romantic—some big happy ending. It wasn't like that at all. The characters were flawed and uninspired. The love scenes were amateurish, to say the least. And the ending was definitely not happy. It wasn't even tragic. It just ended."—Dawson

"Dawson, fasten your seat belt. It's going to be a bumpy life."—Joey

"Unrequited love makes you do strange things . . . I mean . . . you know . . . so I've heard."—Joey

Jen: Actually, I kind of made plans with Cliff tonight. I can't come.
Dawson: Oh, really?
Jen: Does that bother you?
Dawson: Should it?
Jen: I don't know.
Dawson: Does it bother you that it doesn't bother me?
Jen: Should it?
Dawson: I don't know.
Jen: No, no it doesn't bother me.
Joey: Well, I'm glad nobody's bothered.

Pacey: Dr. Rand, I'd like to lodge a formal protest. You never told me I'd be working with a repressed control freek.
Joey: Yeah, and you never told me my grade is dependent upon some remedial underachiever.
Dr. Rand: Well, wonderful. So I see no introductions are necessary.

Mysterious voice on the phone: So tell me your name.
Jen: Drew Barrymore. Look, you wanna play this game, let's cut right to the chase. What's your favorite scary movie?
Voice: *Friday the 13th*. What's yours?
Jen: *The Ten Commandments*. Don't ask.

Jen: You know, now that the proverbial wedge we so fondly refer to as Dawson Leery is no longer between us, we could actually be friends...I know, I know, it's a bizarre concept, but we might find that we have something more in common than just the boy next door.
Joey: We don't have to, like, wash each other's hair and do each other's nails, do we?

Pacey: I'm the drummer for Pearl Jam. You?
Girl: You're dumber than who?

Pacey: Please don't make me eat dinner with the Stepford family.
Joey: Uh oh, touble in paradise? I guess I can scrape something up. I think I saw some rat droppings behind the oven.
Pacey: Great. I'll take 'em. Toss 'em in the microwave, warm 'em up, you know . . . .
Joey: That was weird. For a second there, I was overcome with this wave of sympathy for you . . . . it'll pass.

Dawson:  I just want to let you know that I completely understand the absurdity of this moment.  I actually thought of sending over a drink or saying something clever . . . what's your sign?  I figured directness would be the best approach—i.e. "My name is Dawson."  Not that my name in and of itself should impress you, but kind of in the hopes that you might, in response, tell me your name.

Nina:  Did it occur to you that maybe I'm just not interested?

Dawson:  No, but blind optimism is one of my faults.

Nina:  One of your faults?  Do you have many?

Dawson:  Let's see.  There's my reckless disregard for danger.  My tiresome romanticism.  And then of course, there's the way that I keep talking long after the person I'm trying to impress has lost all interest.

Joey:  [*The English Patient*] is the only thing that's put the baby to sleep.  Because the baby never sleeps.  And if the baby doesn't sleep then I don't sleep.  And if I don't sleep, I get angry.  I get irritable.  And I no longer maintain my sunny disposition.  So, Pacey, if you have even the slightest bit of human decency you'll rent this movie to me immediately and bring one hundred and eighty-one minutes of peace in my otherwise wretched life.  Please?

Pacey:  Alright, but in my professional opinion, you don't need a video store, you need a pharmacy.

Dawson: Joe, let's assess. What have we learned from tonight's 90210 evening?

Joey: That we should always stay home on a Saturday night and watch movies because the rewind on the remote of life does not work.

Billy:  So this is really it? You are leaving me for a guy who has an E.T. doll on his bed.

Jen:  It's a collector's item.

Billy:  It is a doll.

Bessie:  He's still our father.

Joey:  Yeah.  Our father who art in prison.

She's . . . great  I mean, she's . . . she's smart, she's beautiful, she's funny.  She's a big old scaredy-cat.  If you creep up from behind her, she'll jump out of her skin.  It's pretty amusing.  She's honest—she calls them just like she sees them.  You can always count on getting the truth from Joey, even if the truth hurts.  She's stubborn—we fight a lot.  She can be so frustrating sometimes.  But she's a really, really good friend.  And loyal to a fault . . . she believes in me.  And I'm a dreamer, so I mean it's good to have someone like that in my life. If she goes away, I don't know what I'm gonna do . . . I mean she's . . . she's my best friend.  She's more than that.  But . . . she's everything."—Dawson

"It's all about romance . . . and Chap Stick."—Mr. Leery

"You're the sea creature from your own movie."—Joey to Dawson

Dawson:  When you broke up with me, among the many questions I asked you was "Why?" Do you remember that?  And do you remember your response?  Your very convincing, very heartfelt response?  That you needed to be alone.  That there were too many men in your life, and you needed time away from those men.  And correct me if I'm wrong, Jen, but Cliff Elliot isn't exactly with the women's auxiliary.

Jen:  He's a date, alright?  It's not like I'm planning an engagement party.

# KEEP IN TOUCH

The best way to visit Capeside is through Dawson's Desktop—available only at the official *Dawson's Creek* web site at **www.dawsonscreek.com**. Meet other *Dawson's Creek* fans, create your own home page, read Dawson's journal and e-mails, play games and hang out with Dawson and the gang in Capeside.

# SKILLS I[

# HOME
# ECONOMICS

# F[O]OD

Home Economics 15

Jenny Ridgwell

# HEINEMANN
# EDUCATIONAL

**Heinemann Educational a division
of Heinemann Educational Books Ltd**
Halley Court, Jordan Hill, Oxford OX2 8EJ

OXFORD LONDON EDINBURGH
MELBOURNE SYDNEY AUCKLAND
IBADAN NAIROBI GABORONE
HARARE KINGSTON PORTSMOUTH
NH (USA)
SINGAPORE MADRID

First published 1988
Reprinted 1988, 1989

**British Library Cataloguing in Publication Data**

Ridgwell, Jenny
  Skills in home economics: food
  1. Food
  I. Title
  641.3      TX354

ISBN 0 435 42000 3

Designed and produced by
The Pen & Ink Book Co. Ltd., Huntingdon

Printed and bound in Spain by Mateu Cromo

**Acknowledgements**

Thanks are due to the following for permission to reproduce copyright material: Allied Bakeries Ltd. for the chart on p.7; Anchor Foods Ltd. for the label on p.13; China National Cereals, Oils and Foodstuffs for the label on pp.54-5; Gibbs Dental Division Mentadent for the diagrams (adapted) on p.16; Rita Greer for the healthy eating logos on p.46 (right); H.J. Heinz Co. Ltd. for the advertisement on p.67; Health Education Authority for the information on 'How to eat less fat' on p.8 and for the '10 point codes' table on p.93; The Controller of Her Majesty's Stationery Office, *National Food Survey*, 1984 for the figures for the chart on p.10; Nabisco Brands (UK) Ltd. for the chart on p.28; National Dairy Council for 'The Composition of Milk' chart and for the information in the 'Milk Know How' table on p.68; Oxford University Press for the diagrams from *Home Economics in Action: Food* by J. Christian Carter, 1986, on p.20, and for the bar chart from *Food Tables* by A.E. Bender and D.A. Bender, 1986, on p.72; Potato Marketing Board for the 'Energy comparison' and the 'Popular potatoes' charts on

p.64; Princes-Buitoni Ltd. for the label on p.55; Rawalpindi Tandoori Restaurant for the menu (adapted) on p.38; J. Sainsbury plc for the food labels on pp.12, 13, 18, 43 and 72; St Ivel Ltd. for the yoghurt, cheese and Gold labels on pp.12-13; Tesco Stores Ltd. for the Healthy eating logos on p.46 (left) and for the label on p.75; *Times Newspapers Ltd.* for the article 'Hospital food poisoning spread by beef left out on warm day' by Craig Seton, of 11 September 1984, on p.92; Weetabix Ltd. for the label on p.46; Wimpy International for the chart on p.34.

Thanks are also due to the following for permission to reproduce photographs: The British Museum (reproduced by courtesy of the Trustees of) p.48; Martin Mayer/Network p.29; Cliff Morgan p.71; Pasta Information Centre p.54; John Radcliffe/Science Photo Library p.85; Safeway Foodstores Ltd. p.59; Wimpy International p.34.

Cover illustration by Pat Thorne.

# Contents

_Skills in Home Economics_ gives a lively and colourful approach to investigations into Home Economics. Information is intended to be thought-provoking, using problem-solving as a way of learning. All work has been tested by pupils of lower secondary school age and vocabulary, questions and investigations have been adapted to meet their needs. The important aspect which came over in testing was **enjoyment**. The pupils genuinely enjoyed completing the tasks. When they found the work dull or tedious, then the text or idea was rethought or removed. The book is intended as a 'spark' for ideas leading up to GCSE Home Economics Food courses.

Where possible, real examples of labels, menus, data and newspaper articles have been used. This introduces pupils to the real world as well as supplying up-to-date resources and information.

The text involves cross-curricular activities, with a strong emphasis on mathematics, an important tool when recording results of investigations. Graphs, bar charts and pie charts, from which pupils can extract information, have been used. They are also shown how to construct – carefully – their own. Everyday authentic examples are used where possible. Pupils discover information and evolve ideas for themselves. In practice this opened the floodgates of information provided by the pupils themselves and proved most rewarding. A few recipes have been included and where food has been investigated, suggestions have been made for ways it can be eaten. Occasionally the text has been lifted by a funny anecdote, which amuses the author and her pupils, but has little intellectual value. Symbols have been used to show the type of work or activity intended for each section:

written work to be done

 needs other books for help

recipes to follow and eat

practical work to look carefully and examine something

 discussion with rest of group and/or teacher

A symbol has been used to solve mathematical and other problems. This was jokingly to be called Pea Brain, but so as not to offend, it remains nameless. The symbol guides pupils through a problem, so that they can work on their own.

The author would like to thank Sue Walton, the publisher, and Louise Davies for their encouragement and the pupils of Hurlingham and Chelsea School and Park House Middle School for their enthusiasm in testing the work. Also Mark, Annabel and Simon Ridgwell for their support. Many ideas have stemmed from others and their imagination is appreciated.

In the past few years many ideas about diet and health have changed. Several important reports have been written, known as NACNE, COMA and JACNE to help us with our choice of food and ways of cooking it.

But the way we live is just as important as what we eat. Regular exercise helps keep us fit and makes our bodies work better. This means brisk exercise for about 20 minutes each day. Also it is better not to smoke, take drugs or drink too much beer and wine.

# What's wrong with the food we eat?

In Britain eating habits are changing. We eat more ready-made foods and visit snack bars and restaurants more often.

Scientists have found that we eat:

- too much fat
- too much sugar
- too much salt
- too little fibre.

Poor eating habits are making us:

- too fat
- suffer from heart disease and heart attacks
- have tooth decay
- suffer from upset stomachs, piles and even cancer of the large intestine
- suffer from high blood pressure and diabetes.

Health experts agree that we should follow a few simple rules for healthy eating:

- eat more fibre-rich foods. They recommend 25 – 30 grams of fibre a day
- eat less fatty food, especially saturated fat from animal foods
- eat less salty food. They suggest no more than 4 grams of salt a day
- eat less sugar. Cut down on sweets and chocolates
- eat a wide variety of things we like.

## Quick Quiz

1. How much of the following should we eat each day?  a) fibre  b) salt
2. Apart from a sensible diet how else can we keep healthy?
3. What health problems are caused by poor eating habits?

# To do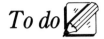

Use the chart opposite to answer the following questions.

1 On the chart opposite, foods with a tick (✓), beside them should be eaten more often than those with a cross (x). Write two or three sentences to explain what you think is meant by 'healthy eating'.

2 Fill in the chart below, adding examples of your own.

| _Foods we should eat more of_ | _Foods we should eat less of_ |
|---|---|
| baked beans, peas... | biscuits, sweets... |

3 For one day keep a list of all the foods and drinks (including sweets and crisps) which you eat. Use the poster to help. Copy the chart on the right and put a tick in the box where each food in your list belongs. Some foods may fit into several boxes. Ask for help if you find this difficult.

Below is an example to help you.

|  | _Day 1_ |
|---|---|
| fruit and vegetables |  |
| fibre |  |
| protein and dairy foods |  |
| fat |  |
| sugar |  |
| salt |  |

| _Food eaten during one day_ |
|---|
| cornflakes, milk and sugar, tea with sugar<br>chocolate bar<br>cheese sandwiches, crisps, apple, cola drink<br>cake and tea with sugar<br>chips, hamburger and salad, ice cream |

| fruit and vegetables | apple, salad | ✓ ✓ |
|---|---|---|
| fibre | sandwiches, cornflakes, salad, chips | ✓ ✓✓✓ |
| fat | crisps, cake, chips, cheese | ✓ ✓ ✓✓ |
| protein and dairy foods | milk, hamburger, ice cream, cheese | ✓✓✓✓ |
| sugar | sugar on cornflakes and in tea, chocolate, cola drink, cake, ice cream | ✓✓✓✓ ✓✓✓ |
| salt | crisps, chips, hamburger | ✓ ✓ ✓ |

Look at the ticks in each box in the table above.
How could you have cut down on sugary, salty and fatty foods?

4 Work out a day's menu which includes more fruit, vegetables and fibre-rich foods and less sugary, fatty foods. Now draw up another chart and fill it in.

5 Design your own poster with the title 'How to choose a healthy diet'.

# WHAT IS HEALTHY EATING?

To grow and be healthy we need to eat a variety of foods but choose more of some and less of others

Eat more high fibre starchy food

Eat less sugary food

Eat more fresh fruit and vegetables

Eat less salt and salty food

Eat some protein and dairy food

Eat less fatty food

We should also drink more water

What is healthy eating?

In Britain we eat too much fat, especially in 'animal' foods such as fatty meats, cheeses, cream and butter. Many experts agree that we should cut down on the amount of fatty foods we eat.

## Why? What's wrong with fat?

Fat is a rich source of energy and if you eat too much fatty, fried food, the extra kilocalories will make _you_ fat too!

Doctors looking into the causes of heart disease, which kills many people in the West, believe it may be due to the build up of fat-like substances in the blood stream. The build up of **cholesterol**, one of the substances, may be prevented by reducing the amount of fat we eat, especially solid, mainly animal fats, known as **saturated fats**.

## _To do_

Use the rules from 'How to eat less fat' and draw up a simple chart like the one below to show how to cut down on fatty food.

| Foods high in fat | Foods to change to |
|---|---|
| 1. butter and margarine → | low fat spread |
| 2. ordinary milk → | skimmed or semi-skimmed milk |

11g FAT semi-skimmed milk

1g FAT skimmed milk

22g FAT ordinary milk

How to eat less fat

Health Education Authority booklet, Guide to Healthy Eating

# TIPS...

Remember, you don't have to follow _all_ these tips.

☐ Choose a low fat spread or a margarine that's high in polyunsaturates rather than butter, hard margarine or ordinary soft margarine.

☐ Use skimmed or semi-skimmed milk rather than ordinary milk. Semi-skimmed milk tastes like silver top with the cream poured off. Skimmed milk has a 'thinner' taste and may take longer to get used to. Most milkmen deliver all types of milk.

☐ Try using low fat yogurt instead of cream. If you do use cream, use single rather than double. And remember that some artificial creams have just as much fat as real cream.

☐ If you like cheese, go for the ones with the least fat.

☐ Use fish or chicken more often, instead of red meat.

☐ When you buy meat, buy the leanest cuts as you can find and afford. Cut off any fat.

☐ Condensed milk and evaporated milk contain a lot of fat. Use them as little as possible.

☐ Cut down on crisps, chocolate, cakes and biscuits.

**Skimmed and semi-skimmed milk are better for you than ordinary milk. They have just as much calcium and protein as ordinary milk but much less fat. But don't give skimmed or semi-skimmed milk to babies or young children. While milk is still their main food, they rely on it for their calories, and they won't get enough from low fat milk.**

# A poem

*Jack Spratt could eat no fat,*
*His wife could eat no lean.*
*And so between them both you see*
*They licked the platter clean.*

 *To do*

Write a poem or short story describing what
happened to the Spratt family.

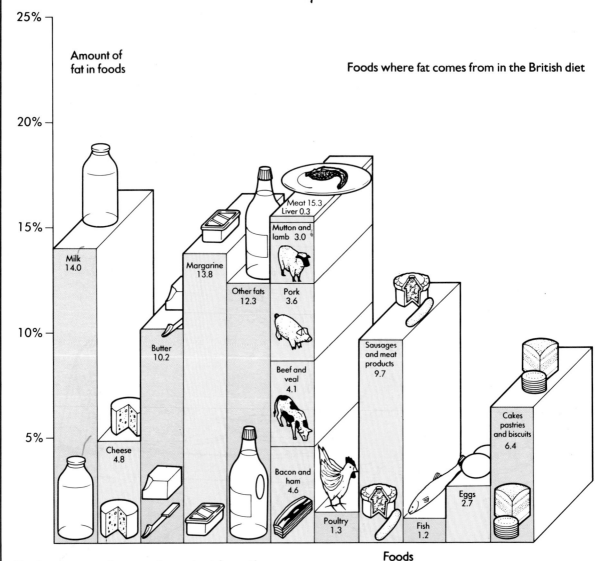

**Amount of fat in foods**

**Foods where fat comes from in the British diet**

Milk 14.0

Cheese 4.8

Butter 10.2

Margarine 13.8

Other fats 12.3

Meat 15.3
Liver 0.3
Mutton and lamb 3.0
Pork 3.6
Beef and veal 4.1
Bacon and ham 4.6
Poultry 1.3

Sausages and meat products 9.7

Fish 1.2

Eggs 2.7

Cakes pastries and biscuits 6.4

**Foods**

Fat is a source of energy important for active teenagers who are growing rapidly. Many foods which contain fat also supply other nutrients. Milk and cheese provide a quarter of our vitamin A and are good sources of calcium. Vitamin A is needed for good health and calcium builds strong bones and teeth.

## Questions

Use the chart above to answer the questions.

1  List, in order, the foods which provide fat in the British diet. Start with the highest – milk.
2  Which *two* groups of food provide the least fat?

3  What foods on the chart could you cut down on in your diet? Remember foods such as milk, cheese and eggs supply important nutrients for good health.
4  People living in countries such as Asia, Latin America and Africa eat much less fat than British people. Why do you think this is?

# Pie charts

The sectors of a pie chart are like the slices of a round apple pie. Whoever gets the biggest slice has the most!

Look at the pie charts on the right. Each **sector** or 'slice' represents something, such as the water content in food. Large sectors represent large amounts of water.

You can usually compare the sizes of different sectors just by looking. Sometimes two sectors are so similar that you need to measure the angles at the centre, using a protractor, then compare results.

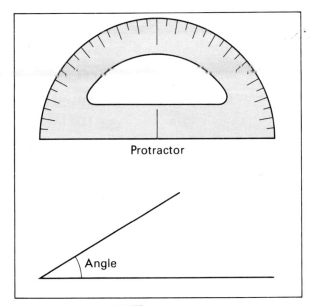

Protractor

Angle

## Questions

Write the heading 'Fats in foods'.
Using the five pie charts, answer the following questions.

1   List the *five* foods in order, starting with the one with the highest fat content—crisps. Fried egg and fried hamburgers are very similar in size, so check each angle using a protractor.
2   How could you lower the fat content of the fried eggs and hamburgers and chocolate biscuits?

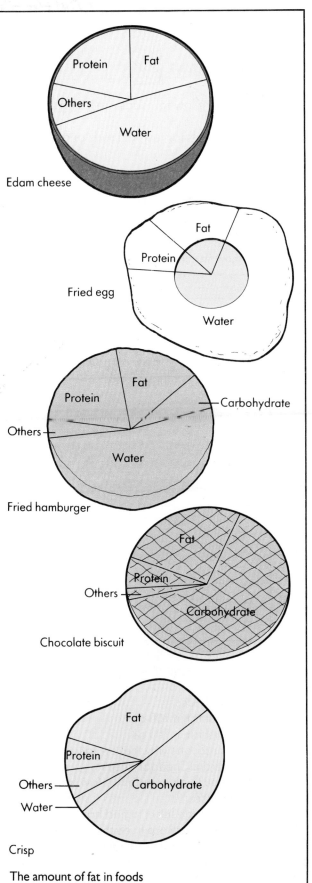

Edam cheese

Fried egg

Fried hamburger

Chocolate biscuit

Crisp

The amount of fat in foods

11

## Investigation

More and more low fat foods are being sold in supermarkets.
Look at the labels for low fat foods and answer these questions.

**1** Draw up a chart like the one below and fill in the fat content for 100 g of each food. You will need to search each of the labels carefully.

Chart to show fat content in 100 g of food

| Food | Fat content |
|------|-------------|
| Low fat cheese | 16.5 g |

**2** From your results, draw a bar chart to show the fat content of these foods:

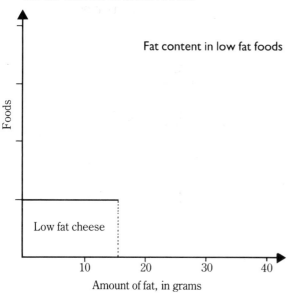

Fat content in low fat foods

**3** Which food has:
(a) the most fat in 100 g,
(b) the least fat in 100 g?
**4** Give two reasons why the low fat cheese is different from Cheddar cheese.
**5** Why do you think people buy low fat spreads and cheeses?
**6** Use the sausage label to find how many grams of fat there are in each sausage.
**7** Having looked at several low fat products, what do *you* think is the best way to cut down on the amount of fat we eat?

**St Ivel Gold**

HALF THE FAT OF BUTTER OR ANY MARGARINE

NUTRITIONAL INFORMATION
Typical values per 100 g of product

| | St Ivel Gold | Margarines high in Polyunsaturates |
|---|---|---|
| Kilocalories | 390 | 740 |
| Total Fat | 39.0 g | 81.0 g |
| Saturated | 10.5 g | 14.0 g |
| Protein | 6.5 g | 0.5 g |
| Carbohydrate | 2.0 g | 0.5 g |
| Added Salt | 1.3 g | 2.0 g |

KEEP REFRIGERATED CAN BE FROZEN
St Ivel, Hemyock, Devon.

Gold spread

NUTRITIONAL INFORMATION

| Typical Contents per 100g | | 39 |
|---|---|---|
| Energy (Kcals) | | 4.7% |
| Protein | | 0.1 g |
| Fat | | |
| Carbohydrate | | 5.2 g |

WITH ADDED INGREDIENTS:
RHUBARB, GELATINE, MODIFIED STARCH, NATURAL COLOURS E162, E163, FLAVOURING, ARTIFICIAL SWEETENER – ASPARTAME, PRESERVATIVE E202.

RHUBARB
VERY LOW FAT YOGURT

NO ARTIFICIAL COLOUR

KEEP REFRIGERATED
DO NOT FREEZE
125 g

Shape yoghurt

NUTRITION

| | PER 100g (3½ oz) | PER SAUSAGE |
|---|---|---|
| ENERGY | 220 k. CALORIES 920 k. JOULES | 50 k. CALORIES 200 k. JOULES |
| PROTEIN | 15.4 g | 3.4 g |
| CARBOHYDRATE | 16.6 g | 3.7 g |
| TOTAL FAT | 10.6 g | 2.3 g |
| of which POLYUNSATURATES | 0.8 g | 0.2 g |
| SATURATES | 4.3 g | 0.9 g |
| ADDED SALT | 1.9 g | 0.4 g |

TYPICAL VALUES (GRILLED)

J Sainsbury plc Stamford St London SE1 9LL

Contains less than half the fat of a typical (small) Pork and Beef sausage. Typical (small) Pork and Beef sausage, uncooked, 9% Typical Lean 43%, Typical Fat, uncooked, 9%

NO ARTIFICIAL COLOURS OR FLAVOURING

HIGH PROTEIN

SAINSBURY'S
LOW FAT
EXTRA LEAN SMALL
PORK AND BEEF
SAUSAGES
MADE WITH EXTRA LEAN PORK AND BEEF

8 oz 227 gram

PRICE     BEST BEFORE (2)

KEEP REFRIGERATED

| Typical Values per 100g | Shape | Cheddar White |
|---|---|---|
| Fat | 16.5g | 34.4g |
| Energy | 270Kcals | 410Kcals |
| Carbohydrate | <0.5g | <0.5g |
| Protein | 27.1g | 25.5g |

Use as part of your calorie controlled diet
St. Ivel Shape is delicious on bread, toast or biscuits and in salads, sauces and baking. For use as a topping, grill rather than bake.
**KEEP REFRIGERATED AND WELL WRAPPED**
**BEST SERVED STRAIGHT FROM THE REFRIGERATOR**
Added Ingredients: Preservative E202. Colour E160(a)
St. Ivel Ltd, Swindon, Wilts.

Shape low fat cheese

Cooking instructions: Grill on a medium to high heat for 5 minutes turning frequently

INGREDIENTS: PORK, WATER, RUSKS, BEEF, SALT, SPICES, DI AND TRI PHOSPHATES, PRESERVATIVE: SODIUM SULPHITE; SAGE, ANTIOXIDANT: L-ASCORBIC ACID; ACIDITY REGULATOR: PHOSPHORIC ACID (MINIMUM 52% MEAT)

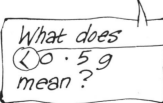

What does
< 0·5 g
mean ?

Sainsbury sausages

## Investigation

Low fat spreads have added water to reduce their fat content. Try making your own.

**You need:**  50 g soft margarine, a bowl, a fork and some water.
Beat the margarine until smooth then try gradually adding a little water.
**What happens?**  The water will not mix in with the fat and separates out.
**How do manufacturers solve this problem?**  Look at the Anchor Low-Fat Spread label below. Buttermilk and water are important ingredients.

1  What chemical is added to stop the product from separating out?
2  Why is this fat not suitable for frying? If you don't know the answer, try it out, but take care!

INGREDIENTS: Buttermilk, Vegetable Oil Hydrogenated Vegetable Oil, Water, Milk Protein, Butter Oil, Salt, Emulsifier E471 (prevents product separating), Acidity Regulators E331, E339 (maintains good flavour), Preservative E202 (inhibits bacterial growth), Natural Flavour, Vitamins A & D Natural Colour – Carotene.

NUTRITIONAL GUIDE 100 g contains:

| | | |
|---|---|---|
| Fat | 39.7 g | Carbohydrate 1.4 g |
| Protein | 7.6 g | Energy 1644 kJ/393 kcal |

Keep Refrigerated. Not suitable for frying

Label from Anchor 'Low-Fat Spread'

< is a sign used in mathematics
< 0.5 g means that Cheddar cheese contains 'less than' 0.5 g carbohydrate
If > sign was used, this means 'greater than'

## To do

1  Visit a supermarket and make a list of all the foods with 'low fat' or 'reduced fat' labels.
2  Design a poster and a slogan for the 'Healthy Eating Board' to help people cut down on the amount of fat they eat.

13

## Eat less sugar

A lot of people like to eat sweet foods such as ice cream, biscuits, chocolates and sweets. But **remember**, 400 years ago sugar as we know it was hardly used at all. So why do we eat so much sugar?

Find out for yourself by asking people of different ages why they like sugar. You can answer the questions yourself too, and maybe think up some more to ask.

## Questions

1 Why do people give small children sweets as treats? Did this happen to you?
2 If you had 50p to spend on food, would you buy sweets or something else? Why?
3 Do you or your friends have sugar in tea or coffee? What makes people start using sugar in drinks?
4 What foods would you expect to be served at a child's birthday party? Why this choice?

## Health problems

Health experts suggest that we cut down on the amount of sugar that we eat. In Britain health problems such as poor teeth, overweight and diabetes have been linked with the amount of sugar that we eat.

## To do

Imagine that you worked for the Healthy Eating Board. Make up *six* rules to help people cut down on sweet and sugary foods.

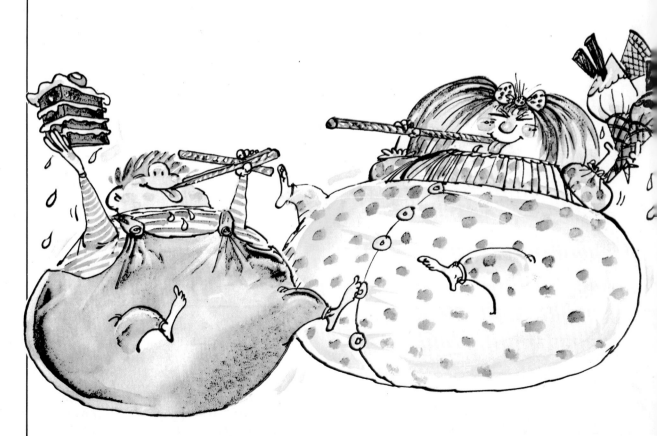

# Effects on teeth

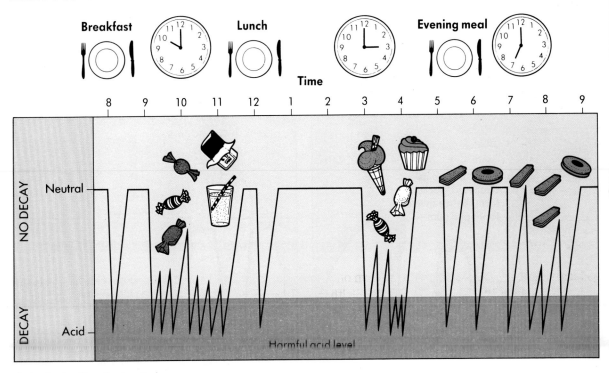

A day in the life of a tooth

Sticky, sweet foods are bad for teeth because the sugar they contain is changed to acid by bacteria. This acid attacks the enamel on the teeth and causes decay.

Look at the graph, 'A day in the life of a tooth'. It shows that within two minutes of eating sugar, acid is produced in the mouth, which stays there for half an hour. So if in one day you eat a sweet every half hour, acid is produced all day. Ideal for tooth decay!

## Questions

Use the graph to answer these questions.

1 What sort of foods are eaten at 10 o'clock, 3 o'clock and in the evening?
2 What happens to the acid level during these times?
3 From questions 1 and 2, what do you think is the effect of eating sweets between meals?
4 Draw your own graph to show what happens if you eat a sweet every half hour of the day.
5 If you ate all your sweets in one go, your mouth would stay acid for one hour. Make up *three* simple rules with the title 'Healthy Teeth and Gums'.

15

Are your teeth really clean? Did you know more teeth are lost through gum disorders than tooth decay?

**1** Soon after cleaning your teeth, bacteria gather and multiply around the gums and between your teeth. Millions of bacteria form dental **plaque**, the 'furry feeling' on your teeth.

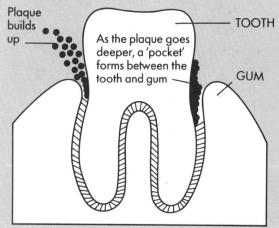

Plaque builds up

As the plaque goes deeper, a 'pocket' forms between the tooth and gum

TOOTH

GUM

**2** Dental plaque is the main cause of decay and gum disease. Sweets and sugary foods are changed by the bacteria in plaque into acids. These acids eat into tooth enamel and decay begins.

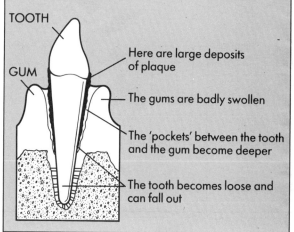

TOOTH

GUM

Here are large deposits of plaque

The gums are badly swollen

The 'pockets' between the tooth and the gum become deeper

The tooth becomes loose and can fall out

**3** If you chew a **disclosing tablet**, the dye colours the plaque on your teeth. Use a mirror and clean your teeth with a toothbrush and toothpaste to remove the coloured plaque. Doesn't it take a long time!

**4** **Gum disease.** The bacteria in plaque can attack and loosen gums around the teeth. It can cause tooth loss.

# How to keep teeth and gums healthy

1 Clean your teeth at least twice a day.
2 Cut down on sugary foods, especially between meals.
3 Visit the dentist regularly for check-ups.

## To do

Design a poster with the title 'Healthy Teeth and Gums' to use in your school.

# Sugar in food

Each person in Britain eats on average 38 kilos of sugar a year. That's 20 - 22 teaspoonfuls a day, either spooned from the sugar bowl or 'hidden' in prepared foods.

# Hidden sugars

Many ready-to-eat foods contain sugar. Use the foods in the picture opposite, 'Teaspoonfuls of sugar in food', to answer the questions.

**Teaspoonfuls of sugar in food**

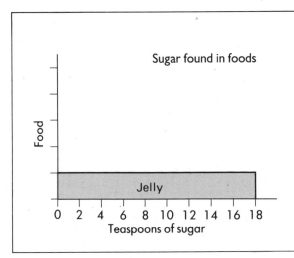

2 chocolate digestive biscuits – 3½
1 small can baked beans – 2½
1 glass Ribena – 4¾
1 Mars Bar – 5½
1 portion jam – 2
ice cream cornet – 2
fruit yoghurt – 4
Sugar Puffs – 2¼
1 small can fruit – 5
1 jelly – 18
3 teaspoons tomato ketchup – 3/4
Coca Cola – 7
1 cup drinking chocolate – 2
1 portion sweet pickle – 2

**Sugar found in foods**

(Bar chart: Food vs Teaspoons of sugar, 0 to 18; bar labelled "Jelly" extending to 18)

## Questions

1 Choose *five* of these foods and write them in order, starting with the food containing the most sugar.
2 Using these examples, draw a bar chart with the title 'Sugar found in foods'. Fill in the chart for the five foods.
3 Invent a two-course meal which uses as many high sugar foods as possible.
4 Doctors advise that we halve our sugar intake. How much sugar should we eat (a) a year, (b) a day?

17

Food label from a packet of muesli

# Questions

Look at the label opposite for the packet of muesli, then answer the questions.

1 What foods are added to the muesli to make it sweet?
2 Why do you think the packet says 'no added sugar'?
3 What fibre foods does muesli contain?
4 If 30% of the muesli contains fruits and nuts, how much is the remaining **percentage** and what foods does it contain?
5 Unscramble the letters of each word to find *twelve* naturally sweet foods.

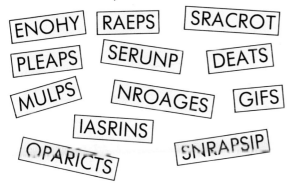

ENOHY  RAEPS  SRACROT
PLEAPS  SERUNP  DEATS
MULPS  NROAGES  GIFS
IASRINS
OPARICTS  SNRAPSIP

# What is a percentage?

A **percentage** is a **fraction of 100**.
So $\frac{20}{100}$ is the same as 20% or twenty per cent.

The % sign is just 100 written in a special way.

Try this example.

If 20% of a Madeira cake is water, then what is the remaining percentage?
  20 parts out of 100 are water.
  So the rest must be $100 - 20 = 80$, or 80 parts out of 100 which is the same as 80%.

Look up 'Madeira cake' in Food Tables and find what nutrients this percentage contains.

## Did you know?

Sugar cane was probably brought to Europe by Arab traders a thousand years ago. People in the Middle Ages ate sugar beet as a vegetable, just like we now eat swedes and parsnips. Sugar has only been popular in cooking for two hundred years.

# Eat more fibre

Foods rich in fibre are important for good health. Fibre helps prevent constipation and other diseases of the intestines such as **bowel cancer** and **diverticulitis**. Fibre-rich foods are useful for weight control because they fill you up, but are not too fattening.

# Where is fibre found?

Fibre is only found in plant foods. These include **cereals** (wheat, rice, maize), **peas and beans**, **vegetables** and **fruit**. The fibre in the cell walls forms the plant skeleton. Animal foods such as meat and eggs contain no fibre.

# How does fibre work?

Fibre cannot be digested by the body. As food passes along the intestines, the fibre absorbs water and increases in bulk. This bulk helps food pass easily along the digestive system.

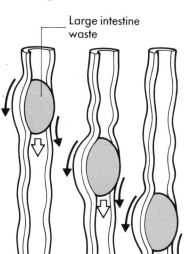

Large intestine waste

Fibre helps waste to move through the large intestine easily

Food passing along the intestine

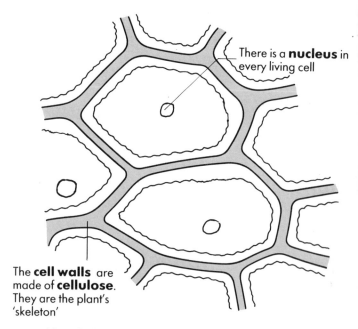

There is a **nucleus** in every living cell

The **cell walls** are made of **cellulose**. They are the plant's 'skeleton'

Magnified section of onion skin to show cell walls

# Investigation

How much water can fibre-rich foods absorb?

**Bran**, the outer layer of cereals, is rich in fibre and may be used for this test.
**You need**:   some bran, a bowl, a tablespoon, water, accurate scales, a measuring jug.

1   Weigh a tablespoonful of bran, then mix it in a bowl with enough water to make a soft dough. Leave it to stand for 2-3 minutes then add more water if the dough is dry.

2   Weigh the dough and then copy and complete the chart.

| Weight of bran | Weight of dough |
|---|---|
|  |  |

1   How much water was needed to make the bran dough?
2   Why do you need to drink plenty of liquid with a high-fibre diet?
3   Why do you think high-fibre foods pass easily along the intestines?

# How to eat more fibre

| Foods high in fibre | Foods lower in fibre | Foods with no fibre |
|---|---|---|
| Peas, sweetcorn, lentils, wholemeal bread, dried fruits, leafy vegetables, brown rice, wholemeal pasta, apples with skins, muesli, potatoes with skins on, some breakfast cereals | White rice, cornflakes, white bread, cucumber, watery vegetables, tinned fruit, white pasta, tomatoes, peeled potatoes, white flour | Eggs, butter, cheese, milk, meat, fish, yoghurt |

Foods containing fibre

## Investigation

Work in small groups.

In your group, choose *four* of your favourite foods from the lists of foods containing fibre. (You could use other fibre-rich foods if you wanted to.)

Now look at a real example of each food and decide how much you would eat for a meal. Weigh the food, fill in a chart like the one below, then put the portion in a bowl.

At the end of your investigation of the four foods, the whole class can display their foods so you can look at the results of other groups.

## Questions

1. Which fibre-rich foods could the class only eat a little of? Why do you think this was?
2. Which foods could they eat a lot of? Give the reasons.
3. From the investigation, explain how you would try to increase the fibre in your own diet.

| Food | The weight you'd eat | Fibre content in 100 g | Fibre in the amount you'd eat |
|---|---|---|---|
| Cornflakes | | | |

Imagine that you lived in the Middle Ages with no packaged or ready-made foods. You might eat plenty of roots, fruits and seeds from grasses or nuts, with a little fish or meat on a good day.

Your menu for the day could be like the one shown on the right.

*Dietary fibre in 100 g food*

| | |
|---|---|
| porridge | 0.8 g |
| barley | 6.5 g |
| wholemeal flour | 9.6 g |
| dried peas | 16.7 g |
| onions | 1.3 g |
| venison | none |
| parsnips | 4.0 g |
| carrots | 2.9 g |
| leeks | 3.1 g |
| blackberries | 7.3 g |
| beer | none |

**Oaty mush**
   Cooked porridge (100 g)
**Pea soup with barley and wholemeal bread**
   soup:   50 g dried peas
            50 g onions
   bread:  50 g barley
            50 g wholemeal flour
**Middle Ages rooty stew**
   stew:   50 g venison
            100 g parsnips
            100 g carrots
            100 g leeks
   bread:  50 g barley
            50 g wholemeal flour
**Stewed blackberries** – 100 g
**1 litre beer**

A Middle Ages daily menu

Remember! This is the dietary fibre in 100 g of food!!

Middle Ages meal

## *Questions*

**1** Use the table above to work out the amount of dietary fibre in the Middle Ages meal.

**2** List the foods you ate yesterday. Guess the weight, in grams, of each food. Using food tables, work out the dietary fibre content for your day's meals. Write your results in a table like this:

| Food | The weight you'd eat | Fibre content in 100 g | Fibre in the amount you'd eat |
|---|---|---|---|
| Weetabix | | | |

**3** We need 25-30 g fibre a day to keep us healthy. How good were your 20th century day's foods? What changes could you make to increase the amount of dietary fibre?

**4** Design a poster called 'Eating more fibre' which could be displayed in your school.

**Answer**
Amount of dietary fibre in Middle Ages meal is 43.2 g.

In the UK, people eat 4½ kilograms of salt a year. That's about 2½ teaspoons a day! Salty food has been linked with **hypertension** which can lead to high blood pressure and heart disease.

As more people eat ready-made foods such as crisps, hamburgers and pizzas, which **all** have salt added, the amount of salt in our diet increases.

**Ready-made foods with high levels of salt**

**Salty meats**: bacon, ham, pork pies, corned beef, salami, sausages, pate, beefburgers, meat pastes

**Salty fish**: kippers, smoked fish, shellfish – cockles, prawns

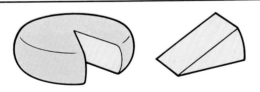

**Cheeses**: all cheese except cottage and cream cheese

**Salty ready – to – eat foods**: salted peanuts, crisps, butter, Yeast Extract Spread, canned and packet soups, stock cubes

We need to cut down on the amount of salt in our diet by sprinkling less salt on our food, getting used to less salty food or using **salt substitutes** which contain less sodium and more potassium.

## Did you know?

The world consumes 169 million tonnes of salt a year. A little salt is necessary in our diet to keep us healthy. Salt can be used for flavouring and preserving food, as a medicine, and is vital in hot countries where salt is lost in sweat. Wars have been fought over salt. The word **salary** came from the salt allowance _salarium_, given to Roman soldiers as wages.

## Questions

1   Make a list of all the salty food you eat on: (a) a weekday, (b) over the weekend. How could you cut down on your salt intake?
2   Look at the list of 'Ready-made foods with high levels of salt' on the left. Write down ten foods which you eat regularly from that list. Why do you like them?
3   Visit a supermarket or look in your food cupboards and find _ten_ foods which have 'salt' written on the label. Did any of those foods surprise you?

Write to Healthy Horace with all your food problems.

Healthy Horace understands.

Dear Healthy Horace,

I work as a nurse on night shifts and get really hungry. What can I take for a snack instead of crisps and chocolate bars?

yours,
Andy

Dear Healthy Horace,

My doctor says I'm too fat and must lose some weight. I really love chips, but what other foods should I cut down on?

Yours, hoping to be thin,
Jenny

Dear Healthy Horace,

I think healthy food is boring but I want to keep fit. Can you help?

Ali

Dear Healthy Horace,

I hate vegetables! My mother is always telling me to eat up my greens. Is she right?

Greenfully yours,
Kelvin.

Dear Healthy Horace,

I want my daughter Annie to grow up with healthy eating habits, but people keep giving her sweets. What should I do?

Annie's mum

Dear Healthy Horace,

I'm getting on in years and suffer from high blood pressure. Salty food is no good for me, but I don't know what foods I should avoid. Can you help?

Hopefully yours,
Mr J. Brown

## To do

Imagine that you are Healthy Horace. Write a reply for each of these letters.

# Healthy eating

Which food belongs to which type of food?
Copy and complete the arrow diagram below.
Draw an arrow from each food in the 'food set' to link it with the 'types of food' set.
Some foods need two or more arrows as they belong to several types of food. In mathematics this is known as a **many to many** relation.

## Questions

1 Make a list of the foods which belong to several 'types of food', and say which groups they belong to.
2 Make up an arrow diagram for yourself. You might choose a 'meat set' with different types of meat (pork, beef...) and then link it to an 'animal set' with 'pig, lamb...'.

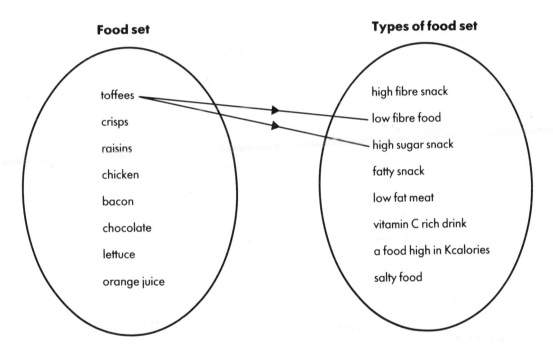

Arrow diagram showing foods and food sets

When you eat a meal after going without food throughout the night, you 'break your fast'. This gives us the word **breakfast** – the first meal of the day.

Many people eat a quick breakfast of toast or cereal and a cup of tea. Others sit down to a cooked meal and some go without, preferring to eat their first meal later in the day.

Breakfast is an important meal for children as it stops them from getting hungry before lunchtime. They might otherwise be tempted to fill up with snacks of sweets and biscuits which are not very nutritious.

Any food can be eaten for breakfast. Different countries often have special dishes. In Northern Europe cold meats and cheese are served with bread and coffee. In Egypt a favourite breakfast is a dish of spiced red beans. Nigerians enjoy hot spicy soup served with fried cassava. In poorer countries, where food is scarce, breakfast may be only a small bowl of rice.

This is the result of one survey of 40 people:

| Choice of breakfast | Tally | Totals |
|---|---|---|
| No breakfast before work/school | ₭₭₭ III | 8 |
| Drink only | ₭₭₭ I | 6 |
| Continental breakfast (bread jam butter etc.) | ₭₭₭ | 5 |
| Breakfast cereal | ₭₭₭ IIII | 9 |
| Breakfast cereal and other food | ₭₭₭ | 5 |
| Cooked breakfast | IIII | 4 |
| Other choices | III | 3 |
| Total surveyed | | 40 |

The most popular choice was breakfast cereals. This is called the **mode** because it was the most common result.

# Make a breakfast survey

Ask 30 – 40 people of different ages what they had for breakfast. The results may be recorded as a **tally chart**. Put a stroke in the box for each answer. The fifth stroke is drawn through the previous four to make it easier to count. Write the totals at the end of each row.

## Pictograms

Information from a survey can be shown more clearly as a **pictogram**.
Here are some simple rules for drawing up pictograms.

1 Each pictogram must have a title.
2 Label each axis (the axes are the lines going up and across the page).
3 Choose a suitable **motif** (symbol) to represent each set of results. Show what each motif stands for underneath the pictogram.

So the breakfast survey could look like this:

Survey of what people eat for breakfast

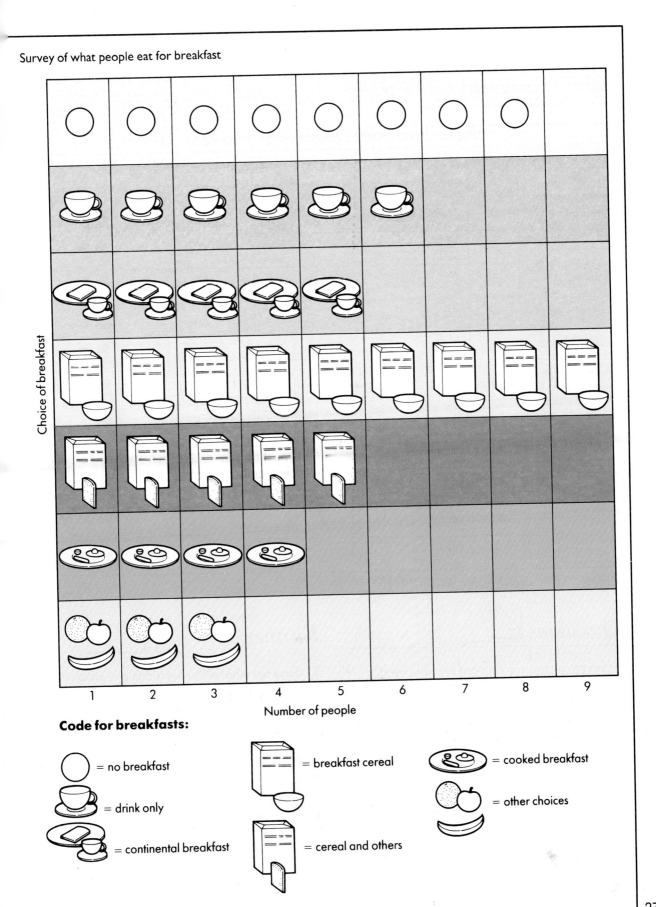

Foodmakers use pictograms so that information is easy to understand:

| TYPICAL NUTRITIONAL ANALYSIS OF BREAKFAST CEREALS | | | | | | |
|---|---|---|---|---|---|---|
| Symbols represent relative amounts per serving | Suggested serving | Dietary fibre | Fat | Sodium | Non reducing sugar as sucrose | Energy |
| | g | g | g | mg | g | Kcal |
| All bran | 40 | | | | | |
| Bran flakes | 30 | | | | | |
| Cornflakes | 30 | | | | | |
| Toasted rice cereal | 30 | | | | | |
| Sugar coated cornflakes | 30 | | | | | |
| High protein cereal | 30 | | | | | |
| Puffed wheat | 16 | | | | | |
| Sugar coated puffed wheat | 30 | | | | | |
| Wheat flake biscuits | 38 | | | | | |
| Muesli | 60 | | | | | |
| Shredded Wheat | 45 | | | | | |

Pictogram showing typical nutritional analysis for cereals

## Questions

From the pictogram find out the following.

1 Which breakfast cereal contains the most (a) dietary fibre, (b) fat, (c) sodium, (d) sugar?
2 Which breakfast cereal contains the least of those nutrients?
3 Which breakfast cereal do you prefer, and why?
4 Which breakfast cereal would you choose for someone trying to lose weight?

## Further work

1 Find out what different foods are eaten for breakfast in the following places: North America, Japan, Spain, France, India, Caribbean, Middle East.
2 Describe these breakfast foods: (a) muesli, (b) salami, (c) parathas, (d) papaya.
3 Conduct your own survey to find out the most popular breakfast cereals. Make a tally chart then draw up a pictogram of your results.
4 Why is breakfast important? Choose a breakfast for the following people:
(a) a toddler, (b) an energetic teenager, (c) a vegan who eats no animal foods, (d) an elderly man who lives on his own.
Give reasons for your choices.

Schools throughout Britain provide lunchtime meals for pupils. In many countries this doesn't always happen, so pupils either take in their own food or go home for lunch.

In the city of Bombay in India, trays of hot food are collected from the homes and delivered ready to eat at school.

Lunchtime at a school in Britain

## Bar charts

A **bar chart**, like a pictogram, can be drawn up to show information.
Here are some simple rules for drawing bar charts.

1  A bar chart must have a heading.
2  Each bar must be the same width and should be labelled.
3  The two axes (lines going up and across the page) must be labelled.
4  Draw the charts neatly using a pencil and ruler. You can colour the bars if you like.

Here is the result of a survey of 40 pupils to find out what they ate at lunchtime:

| no lunch at all | 3 |
| snacks – chips, crisps, cake, ice cream, fizzy drinks | 15 |
| cooked lunch | 7 |
| cold lunch – salad, sandwiches, fruit, yoghurt | 11 |
| other food | 4 |
| total in survey | 40 |

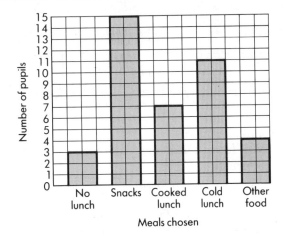

Bar chart to show what pupils ate at lunchtime

# Questions

1  Look at the bar chart on the right. Which type of lunch is the most popular (the **mode**)? Which is the least popular?

2  Write two sentences to describe the results of the bar chart.
3  As a class, conduct your own survey of 30-40 pupils to find out what they had for lunch. Draw up a bar chart of your results.
4  Design a poster which can be displayed in your school. The title is 'Healthy eating at lunchtime'.

# Menus

School meals vary depending upon the local authority and the cooks. Opposite are the menus from three schools.

**School 1** In 1986, the meals cost 35p and were cooked on the premises.

**School 2** In 1986, the meals cost 65p and were prepared by outside caterers who delivered them to the school.

**School 3** In the 1950s the meals cost 2½p and were cooked at the school.

## Questions

1 Using the menus from the schools, for each day of the week, choose a meal that you would like for lunch. Why did you make this choice?
2 Which school's meals did you prefer? Give your reasons.
3 Modern dietary guidelines encourage people to eat less fat, sugar, salt and red meat, and cut down on dairy foods. They suggest more cereals, beans and fruit should be eaten. Which of these schools follows these guidelines? Which do you think is the healthiest meal?
4 Why do you think the prices of the meals are different?
5 Plan your own menu for a school lunch.
6 If you brought a packed lunch to school, what food would you choose and why?
7 For each school, what choice of meal could be made if the pupil was:
(a) a strict vegetarian (who ate no meat or animal products)
(b) from a religion which didn't eat beef
(c) allergic to artificial food colouring?

| | **School 1** |
|---|---|
| **M O N D A Y** | meat pie<br>spam with beans<br>curried beans with noodles<br>cheese salad<br>boiled potatoes<br>raw carrot<br>cabbage<br>semolina and fruit<br><br>Eve's pudding<br>custard<br>apples |
| **T U E S D A Y** | fish fingers<br>sausage and onion<br>corned beef salad<br>chips, mixed vegetables<br>spaghetti<br><br>chocolate sponge and chocolate sauce<br>peaches and biscuits<br>fresh fruit |
| **W E D N E S D A Y** | lamb's liver with bacon<br>braised beef<br>Mexican beans with rice<br>egg salad<br>boiled and roast potatoes<br>runner beans<br>tomatoes<br><br>apricot crumble<br>ground rice tart with sauce |
| **T H U R S D A Y** | cheese, egg and tomato flan<br>roast lamb<br>tuna mixed salad<br>roast potatoes, coleslaw, peas<br><br>yoghurt, steamed jam sponge, custard<br>fresh fruit |
| **F R I D A Y** | American mince burgers<br>cheese and onion whirls<br>ham salad<br>creamed potatoes, baked beans<br>greens<br><br>queen cakes, banana custard<br>custard, fresh fruit |

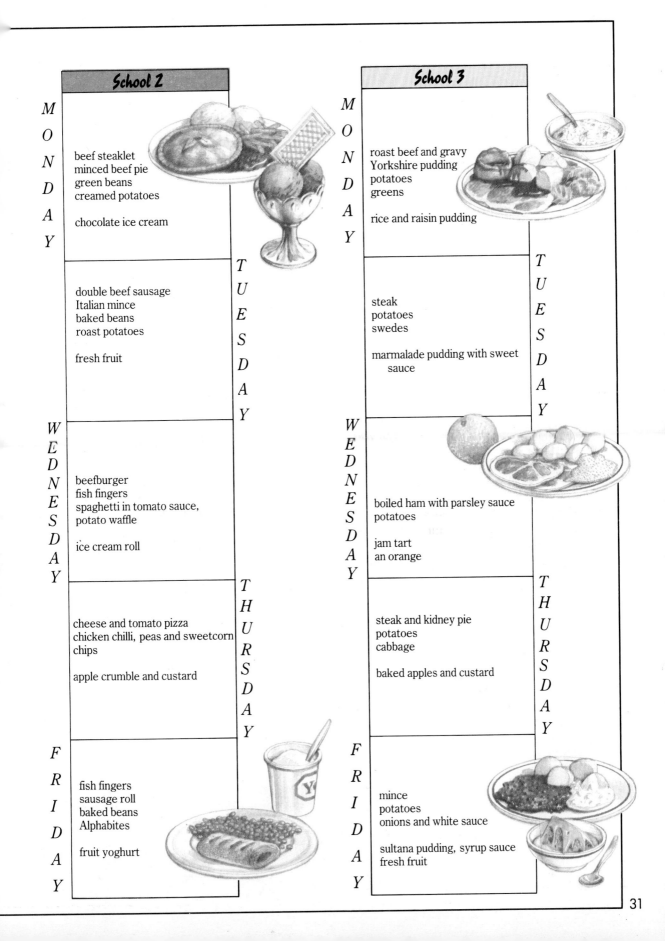

## School 2

**MONDAY**

beef steaklet
minced beef pie
green beans
creamed potatoes

chocolate ice cream

**TUESDAY**

double beef sausage
Italian mince
baked beans
roast potatoes

fresh fruit

**WEDNESDAY**

beefburger
fish fingers
spaghetti in tomato sauce,
potato waffle

ice cream roll

**THURSDAY**

cheese and tomato pizza
chicken chilli, peas and sweetcorn
chips

apple crumble and custard

**FRIDAY**

fish fingers
sausage roll
baked beans
Alphabites

fruit yoghurt

## School 3

**MONDAY**

roast beef and gravy
Yorkshire pudding
potatoes
greens

rice and raisin pudding

**TUESDAY**

steak
potatoes
swedes

marmalade pudding with sweet
sauce

**WEDNESDAY**

boiled ham with parsley sauce
potatoes

jam tart
an orange

**THURSDAY**

steak and kidney pie
potatoes
cabbage

baked apples and custard

**FRIDAY**

mince
potatoes
onions and white sauce

sultana pudding, syrup sauce
fresh fruit

In Britain, more people are eating out more often. Why is this?

From the list below choose the six most important reasons why *you* eat out. Put them in order. You may like to add some ideas of your own.

## Why eat out?

**(a)** It's a special treat for birthdays and family celebrations.

**(b)** You don't have to shop for food.

**(c)** Other people prepare everything and clear up.

**(d)** The snack bar or restaurant is somewhere warm to sit and meet friends.

**(e)** Food is ready to eat.

**(f)** You can try unusual foods such as Chinese, Mexican or Indian meals.

**(g)** You can sit down and have a rest when out shopping.

**(h)** You have to eat out because you are away from home all day.

**(i)** You can't be bothered to cook.

**(j)** Restaurants cook some things better than you can.

**(k)** The family likes to go out now and then to eat together.

## Where do people eat out?

Fifteen pupils took part in this eating out survey. They each wrote down how often they visited each place to eat out during one week. Here are the results:

Eating out survey

| Where did you eat? | How often did you eat there? | | | | | |
|---|---|---|---|---|---|---|
| | 1 time | 2 times | 3 times | 4 times | 5 times | Total visits made |
| Hamburger bar | 4 | 2 | | | | (4 x 1) + (2 x 2) = |
| Fish and chip shop | | | 3 | | | |
| Pizza bar | 1 | | | | | |
| Fried chicken bar | 1 | | | | | |
| Baker's | 2 | 1 | | 1 | 2 | |
| Pub | 1 | | | | | |
| School canteen | | | | 1 | 6 | |
| Restaurant/other place | 2 | | | | | |
| Ice cream van | 2 | | 2 | | 7 | |

# Questions

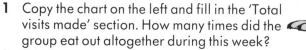

1. Copy the chart on the left and fill in the 'Total visits made' section. How many times did the group eat out altogether during this week?
2. Which was the most popular eating place? Why do you think this was a favourite of these pupils?
3. How many times, on **average**, did each pupil eat out during the week?
4. How often do you eat out each week? Where do you eat out, and why?
5. Conduct a survey of your own to find how often people eat out. Interview 15-20 people. Fill in a chart like the one shown below, then draw a bar chart to show your results.

> I don't understand AVERAGES!

> I thought you liked eating out!

**Answers:**

1. 120.
2. ice cream van
3. 8 times.

## Averages

> Now I see!

Try this example to help you work out **averages**.
If four pupils took part in the survey, the chart might look like this.

| Where did they eat? | Number of visits | | | | |
|---|---|---|---|---|---|
| | 1 | 2 | 3 | 4 | total visits made |
| hamburger bar | 4 | 2 | | | (4 x 1) + (2 x 2) = 8 |
| fish and chip shop | | | | 3 | (3 x 4) = 12 |
| | | | | | total visits = 20 |

So, how many times, on average, did each of the four pupils eat during the week?

Total visits by group = 20
Number in survey = 4

So the average number of times each pupil eats out is:

total number of visits = 20 ÷ 4 = 5 times

**Answer:**
each pupil eats out, on average, 5 times a week.

33

## Wimpy's nutrition chart

| Product | Approx. product weight g | Energy kcal | Fibre g | Fat g | Protein g | Vitamin C mg |
|---|---|---|---|---|---|---|
| Hamburger | 105 | 260 | 1.7 | 9.6 | 13.7 | – |
| Cheeseburger | 120 | 305 | 1.7 | 13.1 | 16.7 | – |
| Kingsize | 200 | 410 | 2.4 | 20.6 | 25.2 | 8.3 |
| Quarterpounder | 205 | 540 | 6.8 | 29.9 | 28.1 | 2.3 |
| Quarterpounder with cheese | 220 | 585 | 6.8 | 33.4 | 31.1 | 2.3 |
| Halfpounder | 305 | 825 | 6.8 | 51.4 | 51.1 | 2.3 |
| Fish and chips | 210 | 460 | 3.2 | 22.6 | 27 | 4 |
| Chicken in a bun | 180 | 485 | 2.4 | 28.5 | 20.1 | 2.3 |
| Spicy beanburger with cheese | 235 | 520 | 15.9 | 22.0 | 16.0 | 17.6 |
| Chips | 100 | 265 | 3.2 | 11.0 | 3.4 | 4 |
| Bacon in a bun | 105 | 280 | 1.7 | 11.2 | 15.0 | – |
| Bacon and egg in a bun | 165 | 425 | 1.7 | 23.4 | 23.8 | – |
| Wimpy grill | 230 | 515 | 3.9 | 30.7 | 21 | 7.5 |
| Wimpy special grill | 290 | 660 | 3.9 | 42.9 | 29.8 | 7.5 |
| International grill | 275 | 635 | 4.1 | 39.7 | 30.6 | 9.8 |
| Quarterpounder special grill | 295 | 635 | 3.8 | 39.1 | 32 | 6.8 |
| Apple pie | 75 | 315 | 2.4 | 13.0 | 3.5 | – |
| Toasted fruit bun with butter | 80 | 265 | 1.2 | 12.3 | 5.8 | – |
| Coffee (with milk) | 0.2 l | 20 | – | 1.1 | 0.9 | 1 |
| Tea (with milk) | 0.2 l | 20 | – | 1.1 | 0.9 | 1 |
| Hot chocolate | 0.2 l | 150 | – | 2.7 | 5.1 | – |
| Thick shake | 0.4 l | 260 | – | 6.6 | 5.0 | 1.6 |
| Small cola | 0.3 l | 100 | – | – | – | – |
| Medium cola | 0.4 l | 135 | – | – | – | – |
| Large cola | 0.5 l | 170 | – | – | – | – |
| Vitality orange juice | 6.5 fl oz | 60 | – | – | 0.7 | 65 |

# Questions

Use 'Wimpy's nutrition chart' to answer the questions.

1   Look at the nutrients found in different burgers. Draw a bar chart like the one on the right to show the fat content of each burger. Why are the bars different sizes?

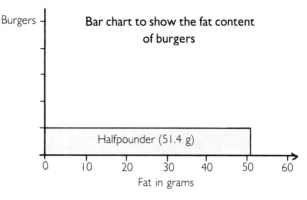

Bar chart to show the fat content of burgers

Halfpounder (51.4 g)

Fat in grams

2   If you wanted to lose weight and had to choose a meal of less than 500 Kcal/2090 KJ, what would be your choice from this menu? Fill in a chart like the one shown on the right.

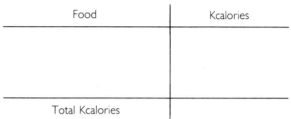

| Food | Kcalories |
|------|-----------|
|      |           |
|      |           |
| Total Kcalories | |

3   Choose a lunch for yourself from the menu, include a drink.

Copy the chart below and fill in your details:

| Food chosen for lunch | Energy in Kcal | Fibre in g | Fat in g | Protein in g | Vitamin C in mg |
|------------------------|----------------|------------|----------|--------------|-----------------|
| Fish and chips | 460 | 3.2 | 22.6 | 27 | 4 |
|  |  |  |  |  |  |
|  |  |  |  |  |  |

4   Which food on the menu has: a) the highest amount of fibre, b) the largest amount of vitamin C, c) the largest amount of fat?

5   Why do you think the foods you have chosen in question 4 have the highest fibre, vitamin C and fat? Write a sentence about each food.

6   Suggest a lunch which you could prepare yourself which might be healthier than the lunch you chose from the menu. Why is this meal better for you?

Papa's Pizza Parlour

## To do

How much does it cost to make your own pizza and is it worth it?

Prepare a simple pizza using exactly the same ingredients as 'Cheese and Tomato Pizza' from Papa's Pizza Parlour. When you have finished work out the cost of your pizza.

# Cheese and tomato pizza

**Ingredients**
170 g plain flour
2 teaspoons dried active yeast
1 tablespoon oil
about 100 ml warm water

**Topping:**
50 g chopped tomatoes
50 g grated cheese
1 teaspoon mixed herbs

**Equipment:**
mixing bowl
teaspoon
tablespoon
measuring jug
grater
knife
baking sheet or round tin

**Method**

1   Set the oven at 220°C/Gas 7. Mix together the flour, yeast, oil and enough water to make a soft dough. Knead thoroughly for 5-10 minutes then press into a flat circle, 20 cm across, on the baking sheet or round tin.

2   Spread with chopped tomatoes then cover with grated cheese and herbs.

3   Leave to rise in a warm place then bake for 15-20 minutes until firm and cooked.

## To do ✎

**How much does your pizza cost?** Work out the cost of each ingredient and copy and complete the chart. To help you the cost of Jenny's pizza has already been filled in.

| Ingredients | Cost of your pizza | Jenny's pizza |
| --- | --- | --- |
| 170 g plain flour | | 13p |
| 2 teaspoons dried active yeast | | 7p |
| 1 tablespoon oil | | 1½p |
| warm water | | 0p |
| 50 g chopped tomatoes | | 4p |
| 50 g grated cheese | | 15p |
| 1 teaspoon mixed herbs | | ½p |
| *plus* cooking cost | | 5p |
| total cost | | 46p |

How can you work out these costs?
When shopping for Jenny's pizza,
    200 g cheese cost 60p
    500 g flour cost 45p
    500 g tomatoes cost 45p.

So can you work out how much:
(a) 100 g cheese,
(b) 100 g flour,
(c) 150 g tomatoes costs?

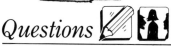

### Working out the cost

This is one way to do it.
If 500 g tomatoes cost 45p
Then 150 g tomatoes cost:
$$\frac{\text{price of whole can} \times \text{weight of tomatoes used}}{\text{weight of whole can}}$$

So the sum looks like this:
$$\text{Total cost} \quad \frac{45 \times 150}{500} = 13.5\text{p}$$

## Questions ✎ 👥

1  What is the difference between the cost of Papa's Cheese and Tomato pizza and your own?

2  Why does it cost more to buy a pizza in a restaurant?

3  Why do you think people are willing to pay more for food when they eat out?

4  Which pizza do you think you would like better – Papa's or your own? Why?

In most parts of the world, the evening meal is the most important meal of the day. The type of meal depends upon what food is available, how it is cooked, and the traditions and customs of the country.

In China they grow a lot of rice, but there is a shortage of fuel, and meat is expensive. So the Chinese eat rice with most meals, chop food up into small pieces and cook it very quickly in an iron pan called a **wok**. Meat is usually served mixed in with plenty of vegetables, such as stir-fried chicken with beansprouts.

Look closely at the two different menus from restaurants. The dishes may not always be the same as people eat at home. Ingredients may have been changed. This may be to please the customer or because what is cheap in one country may be expensive in another. In the Caribbean mangoes and plantains are eaten a lot, but in Britain these fruits are expensive.

**Indian restaurant**  Look at the menu for the Indian restaurant.

## To do

1  Choose a meal for yourself to include bread and a vegetable dish. Why did you make this choice?
2  Imagine that you didn't eat meat. What would you choose?
3  Some dishes on this menu are not really Indian. Which are they and why are they served?

### KEBABS

Chicken Tikka ............................
   (Boneless pieces of chicken, lightly spiced and grilled on charcoal)
Seek Kebab ...............................
   (Minced lamb, lightly spiced and grilled on charcoal)
Shami Kebab
   Minced lamb, fried in ghee)

### TANDOORI SPECIALITIES
Authentic Indian style in clay oven

Tandoori King Prawn ................
Tandoori Chicken (half) ............
Mutton Tikka .............................
Tandoori Mixed Grill ................
   Including one Naan
Tandoori Chicken Mussala – half ..............................................
   Including Rice or Naan

### RAWALPINDI SPECIALITIES
**SPECIAL PULAWS**
**These are mixed with special pulaw rice, garnished with egg omelette, nuts and sultanas, etc. and including small vegetable curry**

### PULAWS
Prawn Pulaw .............................
Chicken Pulaw ..........................
Keema Pulaw ............................
Mushroom Pulaw ......................

### BIRIANIS
Prawn Biriani ............................
Chicken Biriani .........................
Keema Biriani ...........................
Mushroom Biriani ....................

### PHARSEE DISHES
**They are fairly hot, with sweet and sour flavour and including special small Pulaw Rice**

### DANSAKS
**They are mixed with lentils**
Chicken Dansak ........................
   (Off the bone)
Meat Dansak .............................

### CURRY DISHES
**The style and strength of each curry is entirely different from others**

### CHICKEN CURRIES
**(All of the bone)**

Chicken Madras (fairly hot) .......
Chicken Kurma (sweet) .............
Chicken Malaya (with pineapple and sweet flavour) ................
Chicken Vindaloo .....................
Chicken Kashmiri (with banana and sweet flavour) ................

### MEAT CURRIES
Lamb curry (medium) ...............
Lamb Madras (fairly hot) ..........
Lamb and Bindi (medium) ........
Lamb and Spinach (medium) ....
Lamb Pall (very hot) ..................
Rougan Josh (medium and special flavour) ....................
Methi Gosth (medium and with a kind of special flavoured leaves) ................................

### FISH CURRIES
Prawn Madras (fairly hot) .........
Prawn Vindaloo (hot) ................
Prawn and Bindi (medium) .......
Prawn and Brinjal (medium) .....

### COLD BUFFET
**(Including vegetables)**
Prawn Salad ..............................
Egg Salad ..................................
Green Salad ...............................

### VEGETABLE CURRIES
**(Side Dishes)**
**∗No side dishes are served alone –**
**only with a main dish ∗**
**All medium hot, could be changed according to choice**

Mixed Vegetable Curry ............
Bombay Potato (hot) .................
Cauliflower Bhaji ......................
Bindi Bhaji ................................
Brinjal Bhaji ..............................
Sag Bhaji ...................................
Mushroom Bhaji .......................
Mixed Vegetable bhaji ..............

### DHAL (Lentils)
**(Side Dishes)**
Plain Dhal ..................................
Turka Dhal .................................
Madras Dhal Samber (hot) .......

### RICE
Plain rice ...................................
Basmati Pulaw Rice (cooked in ghee) .....................................
Peas Pulaw (mixed with egg) ......

### ASIAN BREADS
Parata Plain ..............................
Stuffed Parata ...........................
Chapati ......................................
Puri ............................................
Buttered Chapati ......................
Naan ..........................................
Keema Naan  ............................

### ASIAN FRUITS AND SWEETS
Mango .......................................
Lychee .......................................
Pineapple ..................................
Mixed Fruit Salad .....................
Julabi ........................................
Gulab-Jaman .............................
Kulfi (Oriental Ice Cream) ........

### ENGLISH SWEETS
Banana Fritter ...........................
Ice Cream (Vanilla) ...................

Menu from an Indian restaurant

Caribbean menu

**Crabes Farcis** — from Guadeloup & Dominica; crab backs stuffed with crabmeat, rum, hot peppers and West Indian spices. £2·30

**Souse** — from Barbadoes & Trinidad; pork marinated overnight in lime juice, garlic and West Indian spices served with cucumber. £1·60

**Stuffed Plantain** — from Puerto Rico; ripe plantains stuffed with beef, ham, eggs, tomatoes, hot peppers, lemon juice and West Indian spices. £1·75

**Callaloo** — from all Islands; soup of taro leaves or spinach, okra, smoked pork, crab, coconut milk and West Indian spices. £2·25

**Grapefruit in Rum** £1·15

**Spare Ribs** — creole style £2·45

**Avocado Diablo** — from Dominica; avocado with saltfish, garlic, tomatoes, lime juice, capsicum and West Indian spices. £2·30

·· ———— ··

**Sancoche** — from French Islands; chicken, salt fish, tomatoes, coconut cream, onions, hot peppers and West Indian herbs and spices. £4·50

**Porc Creole** — from Dominica; pork marinated overnight in lime juice, garlic and orange juice with herbs and spices, then glazed in oil and cane molasses, served in a sauce made from the marinade. £4·95

**Ananas** — chicken, prawns, and smoked ham cooked with pineapple, tomatoes, raisins, sherry, rum, lime juice and West Indian spices. Served in a pineapple shell. £5·95

**Flying Fish** — (when available) from Barbadoes; marinated in lime juice, herbs, spices, hot peppers and cooked in a piquant tomato sauce. £5·20

**Curried Goat** — from Jamaica; marinated in lime juice, tumeric, hot peppers, ginger, West Indian herbs and spices. £4·75

**Pepperpot** — from Trinidad and Barbadoes; chicken, salt beef, oxtail, pigs trotters, beef, cassareep, hot peppers and West Indian spices. £3·75

**Pilau** — from all Islands; marinated chicken, simmered in marinade with rice until tender. £3·40

**Salads** — green £0·80 · mixed salad £1·25

**Vegetables** — subject to availability, portions of plantain, yam, sweet potatoes etc. · mixed platter £2·00

Rice £0·50 · £1·20

Rice and Peas £1·10

V.A.T. included

Covert £0·60

*To do*

**Caribbean menu:** Look at the menu.
4  Choose a meal for yourself, and write why you made this choice.
5  How much did your meal cost?

Some of the foods on the menus may have been unusual. Write down those which you did not know about. Try and find more about them using other books. Fill in a chart like the one on the right with your results.

| Foods and dishes which are new to me | Things I found out about them |
| --- | --- |
| Callaloo | A soup made from leaves like spinach, okra, pork, crab and coconut milk. Made in the islands of the Caribbean |

## Shop layout

Imagine that you are in charge of Wizzos Superstore. Copy out the plan. You have to place all the products below the plan on the shelves and in the freezers and chilled cabinets in your store. On your plan, write where each product should go.

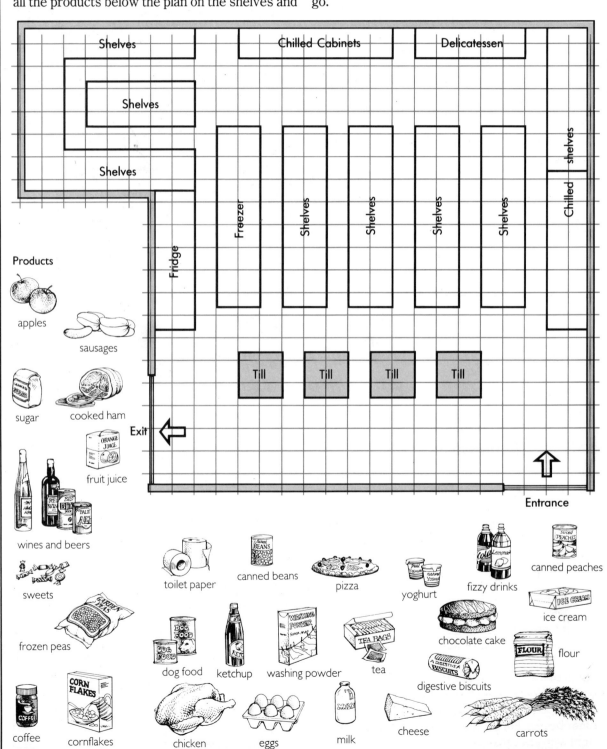

Here are a few tips to help you.

1   You want your customers to walk all round your shop, so place items such as eggs, flour, tea and sugar separately, so that customers visit all areas.

2   Sort out your store into areas. Yoghurt and cheese could be close together as could fizzy drinks and wines and beers.

## Why do people prefer to shop in supermarkets?

Below are some of the reasons why people use supermarkets. Choose *three* points which you think are important and put them in order. Add two ideas of your own.

(a)   Most families have cars, and people like to drive and park near the shop.

(b)   People are too busy to go from shop to shop. Supermarkets have all the goods under one roof.

(c)   Shopping is quick, although sometimes you have to queue at checkouts.

(d)   Supermarkets have a wide range of goods already packed and priced.

(e)   Prices are lower in supermarkets. They can buy goods in large quantities and cut the price to the consumer.

(f)   You can buy *own label* goods, packed by the supermarket, which are cheaper.

Do you disagree with any of these reasons? Write a sentence to explain why.

## Further work

1   There are many small corner shops and specialist shops such as butcher's and greengrocer's. Why do people find these shops useful?

2   Choose a name for a supermarket. Draw the design you would use for: (a) the shop front sign, (b) carrier bags, (c) an own label can of beans and bag of flour. What colours would you choose in your design? How would you decorate your shop?

3   Visit your local supermarket. Draw a plan of the shop showing shelves, freezers, chilled cabinets, and tills. Show the position of sugar, cheese, eggs, flour, sweets and tomato ketchup. Why are these foods placed in these positions?

41

Food labels help you to choose the kind of food you want to buy. Without a label how would you know what is inside a packet? The labels of most prepacked foods show:

- the name and address of the food packer
- the food name
- the weight of food
- a date to show when the food is best eaten by
- the ingredients, listed in order
- instructions for use
- how to store
- nutrition details
- any special claims about the contents.

## What's on a label?

The chart on the right has been filled in for Bloggs Crispos.

Blogg's crisps

**BEST BEFORE**
## SEP 89

Mr J. Bloggs Crispos are made from peeled potatoes, thicker cut than normal crisps, and specially packed in foil to maintain their fresh, natural flavour.
They contain no artificial colourings or preservatives, using 100% natural flavourings. Potatoes are a high fibre natural product and may produce seasonal variations in the colour of the crisps.

e 25 g

We make every effort to ensure that the contents of this package reach you in an excellent condition. If for any reason they do not do so, please return the packet to our CONSUMER SERVICE DEPT., at the address shown below, stating when and where purchased. Your statutory rights are not affected.

BLOGGS FACTORY
MAIN STREET
BIRMINGHAM V12 3DR

INGREDIENTS:
POTATOES, VEGETABLE OIL, SALT

What's in a label?

| Name of foodmaker | Address of foodmaker |
|---|---|
| Mr J. Bloggs | Bloggs factory Main Street BIRMINGHAM V12 3DR |
| **Name of the food** | **What is the food?** |
| Bloggs Crispos | Potato Crisps |
| **List of ingredients** | **Weight of contents** |
| Potatoes Vegetable oil Salt | 25 g |
| **What does the bar code look like?** 50189540 | **How should the food be stored?** It doesn't tell you |
| **What is the date mark or 'best before' date?** 'Best before Sep 89' | **What claims are made about the food?** 'High Fibre' No artificial colourings or preservatives used |
| **How do you know these claims are true?** From the information about the nutrition given | **How should the food be prepared?** It doesn't tell you, but crisps are ready to eat |
| **What other information is given on the label?** There is a 'keep tidy' picture  | |

**SAINSBURY'S**
*— Simply Heat & Serve —*
# TAGLIATELLE
*With mushrooms and smoked ham in a creamy sauce*
*SERVES 2*

**NO** ARTIFICIAL COLOURS OR FLAVOURING

**4 MINUTES**

SERVING SUGGESTION

**560 gram 1.23 lb**

BEST BEFORE (2)

KEEP REFRIGERATED

THIS PRODUCT IS SUITABLE FOR HOME FREEZING

J Sainsbury plc Stamford Street London SE1 9LL

0032 9101

**SAINSBURY'S**
*— Simply Heat & Serve —*
# TAGLIATELLE

INGREDIENTS: PASTA, (DURUM WHEAT SEMOLINA, WATER, EGGS, SPINACH POWDER), CHICKEN STOCK, MUSHROOMS, DOUBLE CREAM, SMOKED HAM (WITH PRESERVATIVE: E250): VEGETABLE OIL, MODIFIED STARCH, WHITE WINE, SUGAR, VEGETABLE STOCK, SALT, LEMON JUICE, WHITE PEPPER (LESS THAN 10% MEAT)

*Serve with lightly cooked green vegetables such as broccoli or with a crisp green salad*

| NUTRITION | TYPICAL VALUES COOKED AS PER INSTRUCTIONS | |
|---|---|---|
| | PER 100 g (3½ oz) | PER SERVING (280 g) |
| ENERGY | 205 K/CALORIES 860 K/JOULES | 580 K/CALORIES 2410 K/JOULES |
| PROTEIN | 9.1 g | 25.5 g |
| CARBOHYDRATE | 9.0 g | 25.2 g |
| TOTAL FAT | 15.2 g | 42.6 g |
| of which POLYUNSATURATES | 1.6 g | 4.5 g |
| SATURATES | 7.2 g | 20.2 g |
| ADDED SUGARS | 1.3 g | 3.6 g |
| ADDED SALT | 0.5 g | 1.4 g |

**COOKING INSTRUCTIONS**
Remove outer sleeve, but do not remove film. Place in a preheated oven at 180°C, 350°F, Gas Mark 4 for 20–25 minutes.

**MICROWAVE INSTRUCTIONS**
Remove sleeve. Pierce a small hole in the film lid. Cook on full power for 4–4½ minutes.
These instructions are based on a 650 watt microwave oven. It may be necessary to alter them for different output models.

DO NOT REHEAT

Label for Tagliatelle

# Questions

Look at the label for Tagliatelle above.

**1** Copy out the chart 'What's on a label' and fill in each box using the Tagliatelle label.

**2** How does the 'nutrition' label help you understand what the food is made up of?

**3** Why are there two different cooking instructions?

**4** Design your own label and fill in a 'What's on a label' chart for it.

Most prepacked foods must have a complete list of ingredients. Those which don't need labels include fizzy water, butter, fresh fruit and vegetables.

The ingredients must be listed in order, by weight, with the heaviest ingredients first. If the food contains more than 5% water, it must be listed on the label.

# Additives

Foodmakers are allowed to add safe substances to food if they are needed to improve the food in some way. These food additives must be listed with their type name plus either their chemical name or number, or both.

A sausage label might list: preservative, potassium nitrite, E249.

## What is the E for?

E in front of a number means that the additive has been passed as safe by the European Economic Community.

## How many additives are there?

There are about 3500 which foodmakers can use in Britain. There are **four** main reasons for using additives:

### (a) Taste
Foodmakers use nearly 3000 different flavourings in food. Flavour enhancers are used most, especially **monosodium glutamate** (E621) which increases the flavour in savoury food. Artificial sweeteners such as **saccharin** are used in foods for slimmers and others.

### (b) To improve texture
*Emulsifiers and stabilizers* help fats and oils mix with water in foods such as mayonnaise.
*Thickeners* especially 'modified starch', are listed on many labels, such as dried soups.

*Anti-caking agents* stop lumps forming in powdery food. So **magnesium carbonate** (E504) is added to salt to help it run smoothly.
*Gelling agents* such as **pectin** (E440a) in jams and desserts help things set.
*Raising agents* such as **baking powder** help foods, such as cakes, to rise.

### (c) Colour
In Britain 46 colouring additives are allowed. A lot are natural colours, for example:
- **annatto** (E160b) – a yellow dye from the seeds of a tropical tree
- **curcumin** (E100) – an orange-yellow dye from turmeric root.

Artificial colours include **tartrazine** (E102), a yellow colour used in orange squash. **Caramel** (E150) is used a lot to colour cakes, soups and gravy granules.

### (d) Keeping food longer
**Preservatives** are used in a wide range of foods to keep them longer. **Sulphur dioxide** (E220) is used to preserve dried fruits such as apricots, and in fruit juices.
**Antioxidants** help prevent fats and oils from going off or turning **rancid**. They are used in biscuits and pork pies. One example is **BHA butylated hydroxyanisole** (E320).

## *Questions*

1 On the list of ingredients, which ingredient comes first?
2 When is water listed on a label?
3 What is an E number?
4 How many different additives can be used in Britain?
5 How many different types of flavourings can be used?

## Labels from different foods

**1**

INGREDIENTS: Sugar, Modified Starch, Vegetable Oil (Hydrogenated), Emulsifiers (Propylene Glycol Monostearate, Lecithin), Gelling Agents (Disodium Monophosphate, Sodium Pyrophosphate), Caseinate, Lactose, Flavourings, Whey Powder, Colours (Betanin, Canthaxanthin).

**2**

INGREDIENTS: WATER, SPAGHETTI (DURAM WHEAT), TOMATO PASTE, SUGAR, SALT, MODIFIED STARCH, ONION POWDER, HYDROGENATED VEGETABLE OIL, HERBS, SPICES

**3**

Ingredients: Flour, Vegetable and Animal Fats, Sugar, Wholemeal Flour, Cane Syrup, Raising Agents (Sodium Bicarbonate, Tartaric Acid), Salt.

**4**

INGREDIENTS: DRIED VEGETABLES IN VARIABLE PROPORTIONS (PEAS, ONIONS, CARROTS, TOMATOES, SWEETCORN, CELERY, LEEKS, RED PEPPERS), POTATO STARCH, NOODLES SALT, HYDROLYSED VEGETABLE PROTEIN, FLAVOUR ENHANCERS: MONOSODIUM GLUTAMATE AND SODIUM-5-RIBONUCLEOTIDES, YEAST EXTRACT, VEGETABLE FAT, SPICES, DRIED PARSLEY, COLOUR: CARAMEL, EMULSIFIER: MONO and DIGLYCERIDES OF FATTY ACIDS

**5**

INGREDIENTS: Sugar, Invert Sugar, Syrup, Glucose Syrup, Water, Gelatine, Natural Colours (Beetroot Extract, Annatto), Citric Acid, Flavouring, Acidity Regulator (Sodium Citrate), Acetic Acid, Raspberry Juice, Lemon Juice, Artificial Sweetener (Sodium Saccharin).

**6**

| STORAGE INSTRUCTIONS | | INGREDIENTS: SKIMMED MILK, |
|---|---|---|
| FOOD FREEZER | ★ ★ ★ ★ 3 MONTHS | SUGAR, VEGETABLE FAT, WHEY |
| STAR MARKED | ★ ★ ★ 1 MONTH | POWDER, GLYCEROL, EMULSIFIER: |
| FROZEN COMPARTMENT | ★ ★ 1 WEEK | E471: STABILISERS: E412, E466, |
| OF REFRIGERATOR | ★ 1 DAY | E407; FLAVOURING, NATURAL |
| DO NOT REFREEZE ONCE THAWED | | COLOUR: ANNATTO. |

**7**

INGREDIENTS: SALT, HYDROGENATED VEGETABLE OIL, FLAVOUR ENHANCER (MONOSODIUM GLUTAMATE), STARCH, YEAST EXTRACT, VEGETABLE EXTRACTS (CELERY, CARROT, ONION, LEEK), HYDROLYSED VEGETABLE PROTEIN, DEHYDRATED TOMATO SPICES, HERBS.

**8**

INGREDIENTS: UNTREATED UNBLEACHED WHITE FLOUR, SULTANAS, WATER, HYDROGENATED VEGETABLE OIL, SUGAR, SKIMMED MILK POWDER, RAISING AGENTS: E450(a), BICARBONATE OF SODA; EMULSIFIERS: E322, E471; SALT, WHOLE EGG

FLOUR USED: UNTREATED UNBLEACHED WHITE FLOUR

## To do

1 Make a list of the headings: 'Taste', 'To improve texture', 'Colour', 'To keep food longer'. Use the labels found in this book and give one example of an additive for each heading.
2 Make your own collection of labels. Use the same headings as in **1** and find as many examples as possible for each section.

The eight labels shown on this page belong to the following packets:
(a) vanilla ice cream
(b) vegetable stock cubes
(c) fruit scones
(d) digestive (wheatmeal) biscuits
(e) strawberry-flavour dessert mix
(f) raspberry-flavour jelly
(g) spaghetti in tomato sauce
(h) spring vegetable soup mix

## Quick Quiz

1 Can you match the packet to the label?
2 For each packet, write down the main ingredient. **Remember**, the heaviest ingredient comes first.
3 Which of the ingredients in question 2 surprised you, and why?
4 Some of the foodmakers have explained what the additives on their labels are used for. For example, on label 7: flavour enhancer, monosodium glutamate. From the labels find *five* additives and explain what they do.
5 Use label 5 to find out what 'natural colours' can be used in food. Can you find others?
6 If the food contains more than 5% water, it must be listed on the label.
(a) Which *two* food labels indicate the most water?
(b) Why is water useful in these foods?

**Answers** to labels:
label 1 (e), 2 (g), 3 (d), 4 (h),
5 (f), 6 (a), 7 (b), 8 (c)

45

There is no law, as yet, to say that foodmakers must list the nutrients in their foodstuffs. Many packets do have charts which list the nutrients of the food inside. They usually tell you the amount of **fat**, **carbohydrate**, **protein** and **energy** in terms of grams in each 100 grams of food. *If they wish*, foodmakers can give more details.

Some foodmakers are adding their own 'Healthy eating' logo to their labels. Here are some examples of the symbols they are using:

**1**

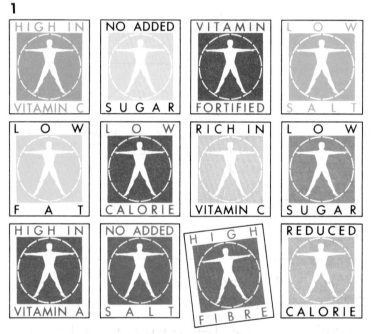

**2**

**3**

Three healthy eating logos

*Questions*

1 Look at the 'Weetabix nutrition label' on the right. What extra nutrients have been listed? Why is this information useful?
2 Use other nutrition labels found in the book, or examples of your own. How are they different?
3 Design your own 'Healthy eating' logos for a packet. Choose symbols for: (a) high fibre, (b) low fat, (c) no added salt, (d) no added sugar.

An average serving of two Weetabix (37.5g) provides at least one sixth of the daily recommended requirements for the average adult of the vitamins listed and iron.

| TYPICAL NUTRITIONAL COMPOSITION | | | |
|---|---|---|---|
| | **Per 100g** | | **Per 100g** |
| Energy | 1400kJ | Dietary Fibre | 12.9g |
| | 335kcal | Vitamins: | |
| Protein | 10.5g | Niacin | 10.0mg |
| Fat | 2.0g | Riboflavin (B$_2$) | 1.0mg |
| Available | | Thiamin (B$_1$) | 0.7mg |
| Carbohydrate | 66.8g | Iron | 6.0mg |

Weetabix nutrition label

Look at this recipe. It will make a dish similar to
the one shown on the packet on page 43.

# Tagliatelle with ham and mushrooms

**Ingredients** *Serves 2*

100 g dried or fresh tagliatelle pasta, cooked
according to packet instructions
100 g cooked ham, cut into strips
25 g mushrooms cut into slices
300 ml whole or skimmed milk
25 g cornflour
salt and black pepper

**Equipment:**

saucepan
chopping board
bowl
knife
wooden spoon
whisk

**Method**
1   Heat the milk and cornflour together in a
saucepan, stirring or whisking all the time
until the sauce thickens.
2   Add the strips of ham and sliced mushrooms
to the sauce and heat for 1-2 minutes.
3   Stir in the cooked pasta and allow the mixture
to heat through. Season with salt and pepper
to taste, then serve.

# Questions

1   You have to design a label to fit round the
dish of your own recipe for 'Tagliatelle with
ham and mushrooms', as shown above. Look
at the design of a real packet (see page 43)
then copy and fill in the following information
boxes for your label.

2   Imagine that you work for a famous biscuit
company. They have asked you to invent a
new crunchy biscuit. Think of a name for the
biscuit, then design a new label. Invent a
'special offer' or competition to help sell your
new biscuit.

| name of the dish | ingredients list (heaviest first) | nutrition label (do not write this in detail unless you can use food tables) |
| --- | --- | --- |
| cooking instructions for finished dish | how to store it | weight of dish |
| best before date | any special points | what it can be served with |

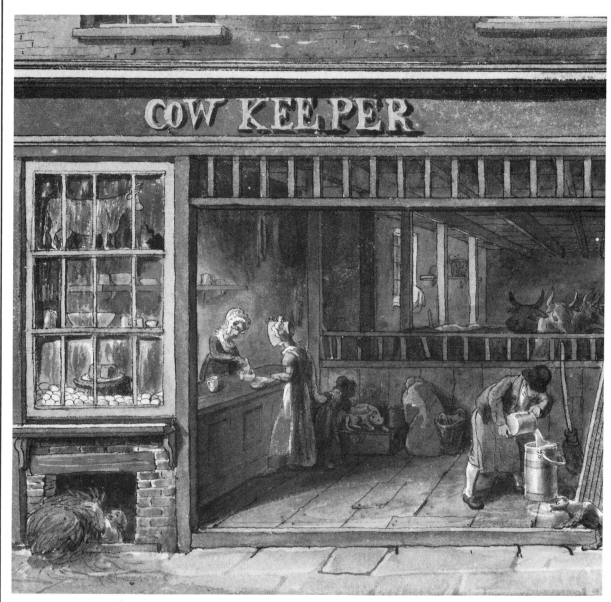

Cow keeper

In the past, food was often sold on the streets and customers had to provide their own containers to carry food home in.

The picture above, 'Cow keeper', shows a lady buying milk in a town dairy over a hundred years ago. At the back of the shop you can see the cows, and the dairyman is in front, pouring milk into a churn.

## Questions

1 How would you carry your milk home from this shop, and where would you store it?
2 Do you think that milk from this shop would be clean? Give your reasons.
3 Today milk is sold hygienically. How have things changed?

Today there is a wide range of packaging available in shops. Many different materials are used such as polythene, aluminium foil, polystyrene, tin and glass.

### Foods

eggs — pizza — apple pie

leafy vegetables — hot hamburgers — apples — milk

fruit juice — butter — sardines — fizzy drink

canned peaches — ice cream — gravy powder — salt

### Packages

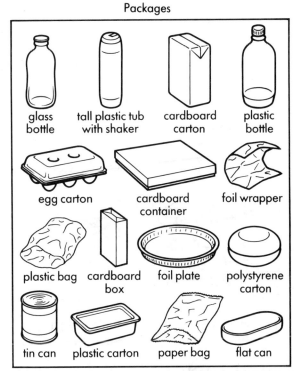

glass bottle — tall plastic tub with shaker — cardboard carton — plastic bottle

egg carton — cardboard container — foil wrapper

plastic bag — cardboard box — foil plate — polystyrene carton

tin can — plastic carton — paper bag — flat can

## To do

1 Try packing the foods in the picture above. Match each food with a suitable package. Use each package only *once*.

2 Write a sentence to explain why you chose the packaging for four of the foods.

3 Design your own packet for a breakfast cereal called **Cruncho**.
Draw out a **net** (flat plan), work out the **design** and **labelling** for each face (flat side), then cut out and stick your box together.
The drawing below shows one design for a net.
Now make up your own.

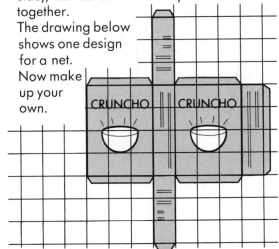

## Further work

1 Look in your food cupboard and fridge at home. Write down all the different sorts of packaging used for food. How can you wrap up food in the home?

2 Visit a supermarket. Make a list of the different materials used to pack foods.

3 What do you think can be done about the litter problem? How could the amount of packaging on food be cut down? Suggest better ways of getting rid of litter and rubbish. Design a poster about litter.

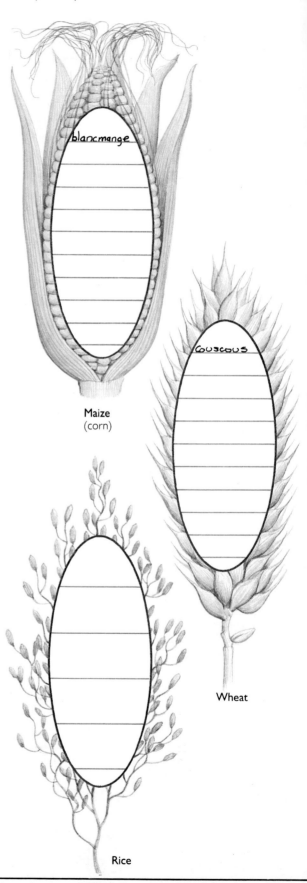

Cereals, such as **maize**, **wheat** and **rice** are important foods all over the world. In many countries cereals are known as **staples** because they are an important food which is cheap to grow and people eat a lot of them. For example, rice is a staple food in parts of China, and maize or corn in parts of Mexico.

Cereals are an important source of food energy, starch and dietary fibre. Healthy eating plans suggest that we eat more cereals as they also supply protein, B-group vitamins and minerals, yet they are low in fat.

*Questions*

1  In Britain, the kind of food that we eat has changed. Why do you think this is, and why is wheat, which is made into bread, no longer a staple food?
2  What is the food value of cereals?

## Which food comes from which cereal?

Copy out the diagrams opposite. Make them larger to fit your handwriting.

Put each of the foods listed below into one of the three cereal 'sets' – maize, wheat, or rice. Use packet labels, textbooks and recipe books to help you. Two foods do not fit into *any* set.

**Foods**
rice noodles, wholemeal bread, digestive biscuits, brown rice, rye crispbread, custard powder, Cornflakes, Rice Krispies, Weetabix, noodles, popcorn, Puffed Wheat, cornflour, ground rice, pasta, burghul (cracked wheat), porridge oats, maize oil, wholemeal flour, sweetcorn, couscous, semolina, tortilla chips, cornbread, basmati rice, blancmange, tacos.

Add ideas of your own to this list.
**Remember**    two foods do not fit into *any* set.

Maize
(corn)

blancmange

couscous

Wheat

Rice

50

# Investigations

## Popcorn

Make some popcorn.
**You need:** 25 g popping corn, 2 tablespoons oil, a saucepan with a tight-fitting lid, a spoon, a plate.

### Method

1 Heat the oil in the pan until hot, then carefully add the corn.
2 Put the lid on tightly, shake the pan and wait until all the corn has 'popped'.
3 Lift the popcorn onto a plate and sprinkle with salt or sugar.

**What has happened to the popcorn?** On heating, the water inside the popcorn turns to steam and the grain explodes and turns inside out, showing all its starchy contents.

1 Draw and label some popcorn seeds before and after 'popping'.
2 Do you think popcorn is a useful food? Give your reasons. When do you eat popcorn?

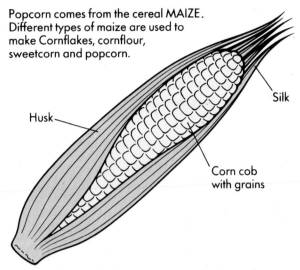

Popcorn comes from the cereal MAIZE. Different types of maize are used to make Cornflakes, cornflour, sweetcorn and popcorn.

Silk

Husk

Corn cob with grains

Ear of maize with husk

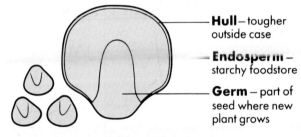

**Hull** – tougher outside case

**Endosperm** – starchy foodstore

**Germ** – part of seed where new plant grows

Grains of maize and cross section of grains

## Wheat flour

Make your own wheat flour.

**You need:** 50 g whole grains of wheat, a liquidizer or processor, a saucepan, a spoon.

### Method

1 Grind the grains in the liquidizer or processor to make a powder. Your result will be much coarser than flour.
2 Taste your flour then use it to make **wheaty porridge** – a dish that has been made around the world for hundreds of years – like this:
* Mix the ground wheat with a little water, then cook in a pan over a gentle heat until soft.
* Serve hot with a little honey or salt.

Bowl of popcorn

## To do

1 Write a sentence about your porridge. Did you like it?
2 Imagine that you lived 2000 years ago. What would you serve with the porridge to make a meal?

51

# Investigation

How can rice be cooked?
Ask members of your class how they cook rice.
You will probably get several answers, but do they work and does it matter which method you choose?

In groups, try out the three cooking methods below.
**You will need:** a saucepan and lid, long grain rice, measuring jug, water, a sieve, a fork, a plate.
In each case, measure 250 ml long grain rice into a measuring jug and weigh it before cooking.

| Method 1 | Method 2 | Method 3 |
|---|---|---|
| Some recipes suggest:<br>1 Boil plenty of water in a large saucepan.<br>2 Gradually add the rice, bring back to the boil and cook for exactly 11½ minutes.<br>3 Drain. | Chinese cook books may give this method:<br>1 Put the rice in the saucepan.<br>2 Stand your 2nd finger in the rice then pour in enough cold water to come to the 2nd knuckle.<br>3 Remove your finger, bring the pan to the boil then cover with a tight-fitting lid and cook gently for 20 minutes. Do not lift the lid.<br>4 Remove the lid and, if the rice has absorbed the water, serve. Otherwise leave covered, off the heat, for 10 minutes. | Indian recipe books may suggest this way:<br>1 Measure 250 ml (a cupful) of rice into the pan, then add 625 ml (2½ cupfuls) of water.<br>2 Boil, then cover with a lid and simmer gently for 20 minutes without removing the lid.<br>3 Take off the heat, fluff up with a fork and serve. |

When each lot of rice is cooked, weigh it then measure the result in a measuring jug. Copy and complete the chart below. Form a tasting panel to taste and compare results.

Try these methods and others using different rices: brown rice, short grain, Basmati rice, glutinous rice...

| | Method 1 | Method 2 | Method 3 |
|---|---|---|---|
| amount of uncooked rice | 250 ml | 250 ml | 250 ml |
| weight of uncooked rice | | | |
| how it was cooked | in plenty of boiling water for 11½ minutes | in water measured by the knuckle for 20 minutes | in 2½ times the volume of water to rice |
| finished volume in ml | | | |
| finished weight | | | |
| what the cooked rice was like | | | |

# Questions

1  Which cooking method do you prefer, and why?
2  Which method absorbed the most water?

# Where are cereals grown?

Look at the three pie charts for wheat, rice and maize.

1  Which two countries in the world produce the most wheat?
2  What do you think this wheat is used for?
3  Which two countries produce the most rice?
4  How is rice eaten in these countries?
5  Which two countries grow the most maize?
6  Find out which part of the world maize came from and how it is used there today.

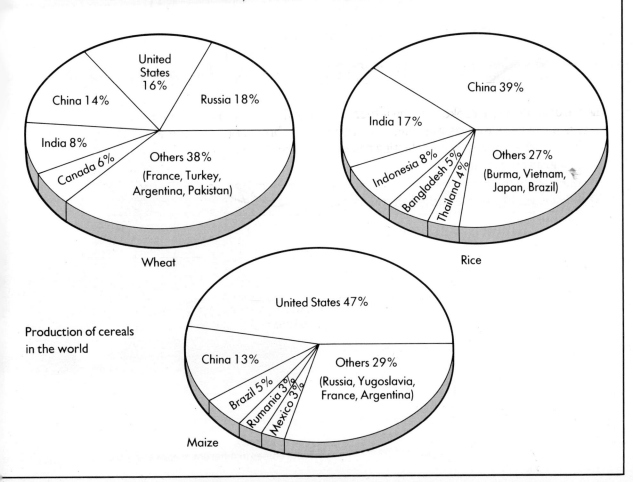

Production of cereals in the world

Wheat
- United States 16%
- Russia 18%
- China 14%
- India 8%
- Canada 6%
- Others 38% (France, Turkey, Argentina, Pakistan)

Rice
- China 39%
- India 17%
- Indonesia 8%
- Bangladesh 5%
- Thailand 4%
- Others 27% (Burma, Vietnam, Japan, Brazil)

Maize
- United States 47%
- China 13%
- Brazil 5%
- Rumania 3%
- Mexico 3%
- Others 29% (Russia, Yugoslavia, France, Argentina)

The Chinese claim to have invented pasta in the form of **noodles**. The Italians think they have perfected the recipe!

Look at the labels for Italian lasagne and Chinese egg noodles then answer the questions.

1 How are the ingredients for lasagne and egg noodles similar? Why are the products different?
2 What wheat is used to make lasagne?
3 How should this lasagne be prepared and why is the cooking different from other pastas?
4 Starting with the highest, list in order the nutrients in lasagne. For example, carbohydrate: 73 g.
5 What does 100 g lasagne weigh after cooking? How has it got heavier?
6 How can you cook egg noodles?
7 Which cooking method is the healthiest and why?
8 There are several languages written on the egg noodle packet. What are they and why do you think they are needed?
9 Look at the photo of different pastas. Find out about as many different pastas as you can. Stick examples on sheets of paper or make drawings of the different shapes. Find out how each can be used.
10 What is your favourite pasta dish and why do you like it?

面粉・蛋・食盐。
INGREDIENTS:
WHEAT FLOUR, EGG, SALT

Egg noodle food label

Pasta comes in different shapes and sizes

**EGG NOODLE**

IDEAL FOR CRISPY NOODLES
OEUF NOUILLES
IMPORTE DE CHINE

净重 250克
Net Wt 250 g 8.82 oz

DEEGWAREN

POIDS NET: 250 GRAMMES
INHOUD 250 GRAM NETTO
NETTO GEWICHT: 250 GMS

中华人民共和国
中国粮油食品进出口公司监制
澳门
PACKED BY
...IONAL CEREALS, OILS & FOODSTUFFS
...PORT & EXPORT CORPORATION
AMOY
...E PEOPLE'S REPUBLIC OF CHINA

煮法介绍
将面放入滚水内煮五分钟，捞起滤干，加上黄油或其他
配料食用，或加各种配料，再炒、煮至熟食用。

**SUGGESTED COOKING DIRECTIONS:**

BOILED SOFT NOODLES.

Cook in boiling water for 5 mins, drain, then mix with butter, salt and other seasonings as required.

FRIED SOFT NOODLES.

Cook as above but after draining fry in butter or cooking oil for 2-3 mins. Add small pieces of cooked meat and or vegetables, salt and soy sauce to taste, then fry for further 2-3 mins.

PRODUCT OF
THE PEOPLE'S REPUBLIC OF CHINA

---

**HOW TO PREPARE** – This pasta does not require cooking when using it to prepare lasagne – just use it straight from the pack (see recipe suggestion)

BUITONI FOODS,
WILSON ROAD, HUYTON, LIVERPOOL L36 6AE

However, you may wish to use this pasta in other dishes such as cannelloni. For this the pasta should be cooked a few sheets at a time in a large pan of rapidly boiling, salted water for 15 minutes. Drain on kitchen paper and use as required.

INGREDIENTS: Durum wheat semolina, egg (4.6% whole egg solids).

It's Italian for good food

**BUITONI Lasagne** ENRICHED WITH EGG

MADE IN ITALY

NO PRE-COOKING REQUIRED

Genuine Italian Pasta

Full of natural goodness

**BUITONI Lasagne** ENRICHED WITH EGG

Perfect Results Every Time

Made from the best Durum Wheat

SERVING SUGGESTION

NOW WITH 50% MORE EGG

250 g 8.82 oz ℮

**BUITONI** ENRICHED WITH EGG **Lasagne**

5 000294 758019

**RECIPE FOR BAKED LASAGNE**
Serves 4 – 6 Ready in 60 minutes.

MEAT SAUCE
110g/4 oz onion, finely chopped
25g/1 oz margarine
85g/3 oz mushrooms, sliced
170g/6 oz minced beef
1 can Buitoni Bolognese Sauce

WHITE SAUCE
25g/1 oz margarine
25g/1 oz flour
570 ml/1 pt milk

Sheets of Buitoni Lasagne
85g/3 oz Cheddar cheese, grated

METHOD
Oven temperature: 180°C (350°F) Gas Mark 4.
1. Gently fry onion and mushrooms in a little butter until soft. Add minced beef and brown thoroughly. Stir in Buitoni Bolognese Sauce, cover and simmer gently for 10 mins.
2. Melt margarine, stir in flour and cook for 1 min. Remove pan from heat. Add milk gradually, stirring continuously. Bring to boil, stirring, until sauce thickens. Season to taste.
3. Place layer of meat sauce in base of ovenproof dish and cover with sheets of dry lasagne. Add another layer of meat sauce followed by layer of white sauce. Repeat these layers of pasta and sauces twice more finishing with white sauce.
4. Sprinkle with cheese and bake in pre-heated oven for 40 mins.

NUTRITIONAL INFORMATION PER 100g UNCOOKED* PASTA

| | |
|---|---|
| ENERGY | 350K cal/1490K |
| PROTEIN | 12.6g |
| FAT | 2.7g |
| CARBOHYDRATE | 73g |
| IRON | 1.5mg |
| VITAMINS | |
| THIAMIN | 0.15mg |
| NIACIN | 1.93mg |

*Equivalent to 300g of cooked pasta

PASTA IS GOOD FOR YOU
Buitoni Lasagne is made from Durum Wheat and eggs and contains no artificial colour or preservatives. It contains over 12% protein and only very...

Lasagne food label

55

**Breads of the world**

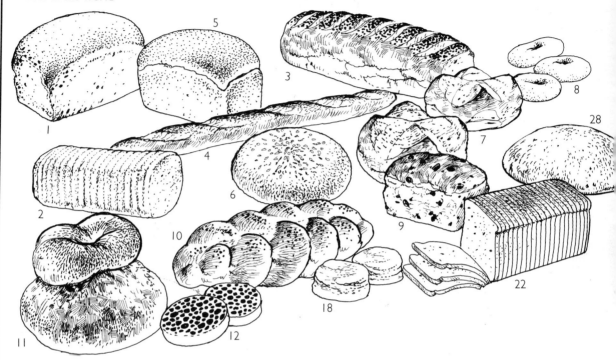

Bread is one of the oldest staple foods. Bread has been eaten ever since primitive people learned to grind grains between two stones to make **flour**. Flour and water formed a dough which was dried hard in the sun. Today there are many kinds of bread made from wheat, rye, maize and other cereals.

## *Questions*

Look at the chart above, 'Breads of the world'. Choose a type of bread which would be suitable for:
(a) toasting, (b) sandwiches, (c) tea-time snack, (d) eating with curry or spicy food, (e) filling with chopped salad, (f) a snack with ham or cheese.
Give a reason why you made each choice.
Choose two other breads and explain how you could use them.

## White, brown or wholemeal?

The ancient Egyptians gave brown bread to their slaves, and poor people during the Middle Ages

ate bran loaves whilst the rich had white bread. Eighteenth century bakers added strange ingredients such as ground-up bones, chalk and wood ash to make flour whiter, as people thought white flour was best.

George III set a good example for healthy eating by always choosing brown bread for his lunch. People used to shout out his nickname 'Brown George' as his carriage went by!

Today we are encouraged to eat more wholemeal bread made from 100% wheat, but all kinds of bread are good for us.

So is it brown, white or …?

| | | | |
|---|---|---|---|
| 1 | Batch | 25 | Pitta |
| 2 | Barrel | 26 | Chapatis |
| 3 | Bloomer | 27 | Naan |
| 4 | Baguette | 28 | Rye bread |
| 5 | Brown | | |
| 6 | Cob | | |
| 7 | Coburg | | |
| 8 | Bagels | | |
| 9 | Currant loaf | | |
| 10 | Plait | | |
| 11 | Cottage loaf | | |
| 12 | Crumpets | | |
| 13 | Malt | | |
| 14 | Split tin | | |
| 15 | Farmhouse | | |
| 16 | Cholla | | |
| 17 | Danish | | |
| 18 | Muffins | | |
| 19 | Vienna | | |
| 20 | Soda bread | | |
| 21 | Wholemeal | | |
| 22 | White sliced | | |
| 23 | White rolls | | |
| 24 | Wholemeal baps | | |

| Bread | Energy | | Protein g | Fibre g | Calcium mg | Iron mg |
|---|---|---|---|---|---|---|
| | kcal | kjoule | | | | |
| white bread | 230 | 960 | 7.8 | 4 | 100 | 1.7 |
| brown bread | 220 | 920 | 9 | 5 | 100 | 2.5 |
| wholemeal | 220 | 920 | 8.8 | 9 | 25 | 2.5 |

Nutrients in 100 g bread

# Questions

1 Using the chart above which shows the nutrients in 100 g bread, explain in your own words the difference between the three sorts of bread.
2 Which type of bread do you like best, and why?
3 Imagine that bread hadn't been invented. What would you eat instead with the following foods?
(a) hamburgers, (b) soup, (c) a ploughman's lunch

# Further work

1 Conduct a survey called 'Using your loaf'. Interview 20-25 people and find out
(a) How often people eat bread each day – once, twice, more times or not at all.
(b) Do they prefer white or wholemeal bread or don't they mind?
(c) What sort of bread do they like best – sliced bread, bread rolls, pitta bread...?

2 Visit a supermarket or bakery and make a list of the different breads for sale.
3 Find out the names of as many different bread recipes as you can. Look in recipe books.

Most people in Britain should try to eat more fruits and vegetables. In summertime there is a greater choice of fruits and vegetables, especially **salad vegetables** such as lettuce, and **soft fruits** such as strawberries. But since canned and frozen vegetables can be bought all year round, there is no excuse!

Why are fruits and vegetables good for us?

- Fruits and vegetables contain lots of **water**, which forms part of every cell in our body.
- They supply us with **dietary fibre**, needed for a healthy digestive system.
- Fruits and vegetables are our main source of **vitamin C** which helps keep the body healthy.
- Green, orange, yellow and red vegetables and fruits supply us with **vitamin A**. This vitamin keeps us healthy and helps us to see in dim light. Spring greens, carrots and sweet potatoes suppy us with vitamin A.
- Fruits and vegetables supply a little calcium, needed for healthy bones and teeth. Dark green vegetables such as spinach, okra and broccoli, provide **iron**, needed for healthy blood.
- Fruits and vegetables contain some **carbohydrate** in the form of **sugars** and **starch**. Root vegetables, especially potatoes and yams, are high in starch, and so also are sweet corn and bananas.

*Questions*

1 Most fruits and vegetables contain more than 75% water. What percentage is the rest? (See page 19 for percentages.)
2 List *seven* important nutrients found in fruits and vegetables.
3 Use food tables to find out two fruits and vegetables which are good sources of each nutrient.

*Questions* 

Look at the photo of the fruits and vegetables.

1 How many fruits and vegetables can you identify in the picture? How did you score?
- Up to 20 – visit a greengrocer's or supermarket and read the labels!
- 20-30 – not bad, look again or use a book to help.
- 30-35 – quite good, so check and try again.
- 35-45 – excellent, you are very observant and know your onions.
2 Vegetables with seeds – for example, tomatoes and courgettes – are also **fruits**. Can you name some other 'vegetable fruits'?
3 Make a list of *ten* fruits and vegetables which are not in the picture.
4 Find *two* recipes you could make using some of these fruits and vegetables.

Fruits and vegetables

Fresh fruit and vegetables are the main source of **vitamin C**. Vitamin C cannot be stored for long in the body, so we need to eat fruit and vegetables regularly. If we eat too little vitamin C the mouth and gums become sore, wounds and broken bones heal very slowly and in the end we get **scurvy**.

Before the Middle Ages in Britain, during the winter months, people lived on a diet of salt meat and bread. Scurvy was quite a common disease. In springtime, however, people could cure themselves by eating green vegetables, and **scurvy grass**, high in vitamin C, was a traditional medicine.

On long sea voyages, fresh fruit and vegetables do not keep for long. In the 15th century when Vasco da Gama sailed round the Cape of Good Hope, two thirds of his crew died of scurvy on the voyage.

Captain Cook's sailors were given limes and were known as 'limejuicers' or 'limeys'. In about 1752, James Lind, a ship's surgeon, set up an experiment with twelve sailors sick from scurvy. He gave two of them oranges and lemons, others cider, and some medicines. The two orange eaters got better, and the cider drinkers did in time, but the others got worse. He wrote a book called _Treatise on Scurvy_ from his results.

Years later scientists began to understand the importance of vitamins. As they were discovered, vitamins were named after the letters of the alphabet. So vitamin C was third! Vitamin C is easily destroyed by poor storage, preparation and cooking. On the next page are a few simple rules to help keep it.

Captain Cook and his limeys

**(a)   Eat plenty of raw vegetables and fruit**
If vegetables are fresh, vitamin C can only be lost in the way they are prepared and cooked.

**(b)   Don't leave vegetables to soak in water**
Vitamin C will seep out from the plant into the water and be lost.

**(c)   Chop up vegetables quickly with a sharp knife**
Plant cells contain a substance called **ascorbic acid oxidase**. If plant cells are cut or smashed, the oxidase is set free and destroys vitamin C.

**(d)   Cook vegetables quickly in a little boiling water or stir fry them**
Oxidase is destroyed at high temperatures, so will not destroy vitamin C. Stir fried vegetables are cooked in fat so vitamin C does not seep out. The more water used in cooking the more vitamin C will be lost.

**(e)   Eat cooked vegetables as soon as possible after cooking**
If vegetables are kept hot, vitamin C is lost.

**(f)   Don't buy old or wilted vegetables**
Much of the vitamin C has already been lost.

# A cook's tale

A cook wanted to plan ahead so she peeled all the potatoes the night before and left them to soak in a sink full of water. Next morning at 9 a.m. she boiled then mashed them, then kept the potatoes warm in the oven until lunchtime.

## Questions

1   How did the cook spoil the vitamin C in the potatoes?
2   Rewrite this tale, using your knowledge of vitamin C.

## Quick quiz

1   What food was eaten in the Middle Ages to help cure scurvy?
2   What was the nickname of Captain Cook's sailors?
3   Which surgeon discovered the value of eating oranges to treat scurvy?
4   What happens if vegetables are left to soak in water?
5   What substance helps to destroy vitamin C?

Today fruits and vegetables reach us from all over the world. Sometimes it is necessary to preserve them so that they keep longer. Foodmakers can use them with other foods or make them into fruit or vegetable juices, jams and pickles which are easy to use.

## Questions

1  Choose one of the groups of _four_ fruits and vegetables. Link each fruit or vegetable with the different ways they can be sold. Use an arrow diagram like the one below.

_Groups of fruits and vegetables_

| group 1 | group 2 | group 3 |
|---|---|---|
| oranges | peas | bananas |
| cabbage | onions | grapes |
| strawberries | apples | carrots |
| potatoes | tomatoes | green beans |

Arrow diagram showing ways they can be sold

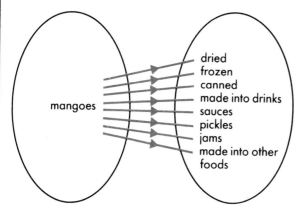

2  Some of the fruits and vegetables are made into other foods. Give examples from your four choices. For example, mangoes are made into special ice creams, mixed into tropical drinks, and green mangoes make special chutney.

## Exotic fruits

Choose one of these exotic fruits and as a group, or on your own, plan a 5 minute talk. Use recipe and other books, as well as encylopaedias, to help you. You could write to companies such as the Fresh Fruit and Vegetable Information Bureau for information. You could even write your notes on paper cut to the shape of your fruit!

coconut

banana

mango

pomegranate

pineapple

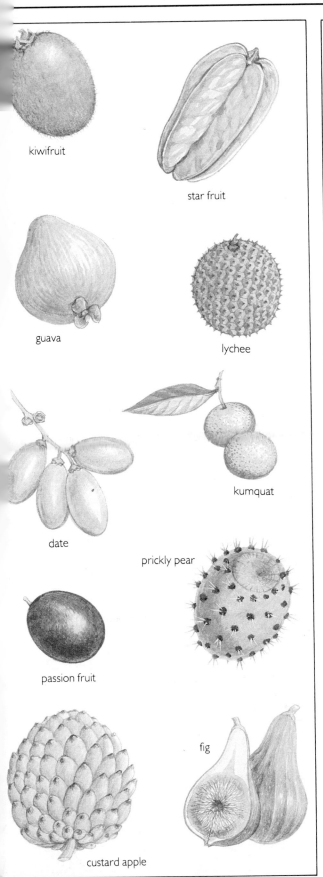

kiwifruit

star fruit

guava

lychee

date

kumquat

prickly pear

passion fruit

custard apple

fig

Here is an example of what you could find out.

**Fruit:** Plantain

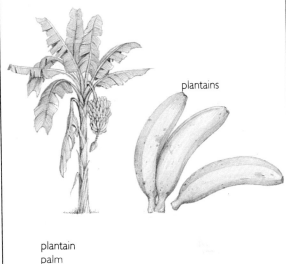

plantains

plantain
palm

*Does it have other names?*
Sometimes called cooking banana.
*What does it look like?*
A long green or yellow banana.
*What does it taste like?*
A starchy, dry, banana when raw. The green
one tastes like potato, when cooked. The
brown/ yellow plantain is sweet when cooked.
*Where and how does it grow?*
In tropical places such as India, Africa,
Caribbean. It grows on large palm trees and
hangs down in bunches called **hands**.
*Where can you buy it?*
In supermarkets and Asian or Indian stores.
*How do you choose a plantain?*
Green plantains are unripe but can be used in
cooking. Ripe plantains turn from yellow to
brown and become soft.
*How can it be used?*
Green plantains can be boiled and eaten like
potatoes. Plantain chips sprinkled with chilli
powder are a popular snack. Ripe plantains are
delicious baked in their skins then sprinkled
with brown sugar and rum!

63

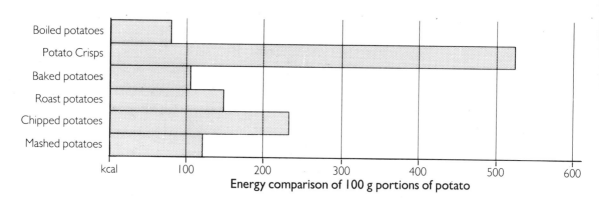

Energy comparison of 100 g portions of potato

## To do ✏️🔍

Look at the bar chart above, 'Energy comparisons of 100 g portions of potato'.

1 Which way of serving potatoes gives:
   (a) the highest amount of energy (in Kcals)?
   (b) the lowest amount of energy (in Kcals)?
2 Why do chips (chipped potatoes) have a higher energy value than mashed or baked potatoes?
3 Look at the section opposite, 'Popular potatoes'. Which do you think are the *five* most important points? Under the title 'Tips on potatoes', write the points in order.
4 Find out:
   (a) why it is better to serve potatoes with their skins on,
   (b) why potatoes should be cooked in a little water and served immediately,
   (c) why potatoes should be stored in cool, dark places.
5 Vitamin C is important for good health. If potatoes can provide one third of our daily needs (30 mg) then what amount of vitamin C might they provide in one day?
6 We each eat, on average, 111 kg potatoes a year. How much is this a week? Find out how much a medium potato weighs then work out how many potatoes we each eat a week.

## Popular Potatoes

- Always serve potatoes with their skins on.
- Always cook potatoes in the minimum amount of water and then use it for making gravies and soups.
- Always serve cooked potatoes immediately — the longer they are kept warm the greater the loss of Vitamin C.
- Use potatoes to thicken soups and casseroles instead of flour.
- Use natural yogurt to mash potatoes instead of milk and butter

- Cut potatoes into equal sized pieces — to ensure even cooking.
- Boil potatoes slowly — to avoid them breaking down.
- Add lemon juice during cooking — to avoid after-cooking blackening.
- Always store potatoes in a cool, dry and dark place.
- Always remove potatoes from polythene bags as condensation can cause them to rot.
- Buy new potatoes as you need them so they are always fresh and flavourful.

What are Kcal and KJ?

Energy is measured in **calories** or **joules**. As both units are very small, **kilocalories** and **kilojoules** are used instead.
- kilocalories (kcal, Kcal) contain 1000 calories
- kilojoules (kj, KJ) contain 1000 joules.

# *To do*

Grow your own vegetables in class.
For years the Chinese have been growing seeds to eat as beansprouts which they use in stir fried vegetables and spring rolls. Beansprouts must be the freshest vegetable we know, since they are still growing when we eat them.

**Indoor seed greenhouse:**  If you use a plastic bottle with a black base, like those which hold lemonade, ginger ale or some other fizzy drink, you can make a container to grow the seeds, which will not need regular watering.

**You need:**  plastic bottles with black bases, scissors, paper towel, a dish, some seeds – mung beans, apple, orange, melon or sesame seeds, cress, dried beans.

## Method

① Remove the label and rinse out the bottle.

② Pull off the plastic base.

③ If the black base does not have holes, make some with a skewer or scissors.

④ Cut the bottle in half with scissors. One end is the dome.

⑤ Put some wet folded paper towels in the black base. Sprinkle over some seeds.

⑥ Fix the dome into the black base. Place in a dish of water and leave in a warm, light place.

**Tips**   Do not let the dish get dry. In a few days the beans begin to sprout. The small seeds usually sprout first, the larger seeds later. You can plant the seeds in soil in a yoghurt pot and grow small plants if you wish.

Most root vegetables contain larger amounts of **starch** than leafy vegetables do. Starch is a source of food energy.
Do potatoes, swedes or sweet potatoes contain starch?

# *Investigation*

**You need:**   cooked potato, swede or sweet potato (or you could use potato powder mixed with water), white plate, dropper pipette, iodine solution.

## Method

1  Put a little of the mashed vegetable on a plate and add 1-2 drops of iodine solution using the pipette. The colour will change to blue/black if starch is present.
2  **Throw away** the vegetable and wash up, well away from food.

**Iodine is poisonous!**

For thousands of years beans have been an important food in many parts of the world. The Romans grew beans for eating, to feed their cattle, and to enrich the soil. During the winter, beans could be dried then made into nourishing soups, stews and breads. For many people, beans were and are a cheap, nutritious food, containing protein for growth, carbohydrates for energy and B group vitamins which help food give us energy.

**Bean Chart**

| Egyptian brown beans | ful medame |
|---|---|
| 2 | |
| 3 | |
| 4 | |
| 5 | |
| 6 | |
| 7 | |
| 8 | |
| 9 | |

## Beans around the world

In Greek and Roman times, beans were used for voting. During elections, instead of putting a cross on bits of paper and dropping them into a ballot box, they tossed beans into a helmet! A white bean was a 'yes' vote and a black bean meant 'no'. So when Pythagoras, that famous maths teacher, told his pupils to keep off the beans, he really meant 'stay out of politics'.

| Beans and peas | Recipes |
|---|---|
| red kidney beans | pease pudding |
| chickpeas | peanut butter |
| navy beans | chilli con carne |
| soya beans | hummus |
| Egyptian brown beans | dhal |
| borlotti beans | baked beans |
| lentils | ful medame |
| peanuts | tofu-beancurd |
| peas | minestrone soup |

## To do

Which bean or pea is used to make which dish? Copy the bean chart and fill in your answers. Use recipe books to help you decide.

## Questions

1 On the bean chart there may be dishes which you do not understand. Find out more about them, then write 2-3 sentences about each one, and find out which country they may have come from.

2 Here are some more beans: runner beans, French beans, broad beans, mung beans, black-eyed beans, butter beans. What do these beans look like? Draw a picture of each bean then colour it. How could you cook each bean? Add more examples of beans to the list.

## Soya beans and peanuts

Soya beans have been an important food in China for over 4000 years. The Chinese call them 'the meat of the fields' since they take the place of meat in their diet, contain valuable protein and are cheap to grow. The Chinese use soya beans to make several different foods: soy sauce, soya milk and tofu.

Portuguese explorers discovered the peanut in South America and took the plant back to Europe and later to Asia and Africa. Peanuts can be used whole in cooking to make soups and stews, ground in sauces and peanut butter, and pressed to squeeze out cooking oil. The peanut is not in fact a nut, but a type of bean.

## Questions

1 Find *two* recipes which use soy sauce and write about them.
2 Find out how soya milk and tofu are made.
3 What are some of the different ways you can buy peanuts? One example is spicy peanut nibbles.
4 Write down the different peanut 'foods' which you eat.

### Silly old bean!

*There was an old person of Dean
Who dined on one pea and one bean,
For he said, 'More than that
Would make me too fat,'
That cautious old person of Dean.*

Edward Lear

## Questions

1 Write a poem or story about what you think happened to this 'old person of Dean'. Try and draw a cartoon too!

### Joke

**What's the most athletic vegetable?**
**Answer:** A runner bean!

## Baked beans

Look at the advertisement below for Heinz Baked Beans from 1900.

**HEINZ BAKED BEANS WITH TOMATO SAUCE**

**AT BREAKFAST OR DINNER** see that your plate is filled with Heinz Baked Beans with Tomato Sauce. It builds up body, brain and muscle. The bean is Nature's most nourishing food. When baked, you eat it in its best form. Served with tempting tomato sauce made from fruit specially grown and prepared, and a generous slice of the best selected pork, there is nothing that tastes half so delicious. Heinz Baked Beans with Tomato Sauce are ready cooked; served in a few minutes.

You can eat them at any time, or anywhere, by themselves or with other food.

**10 MEALS FOR 1/-**

**Points to Remember About Heinz Baked Beans with Tomato Sauce**

They are always ready cooked.
They carry 3 times the nourishment of beef.
Equally good by themselves, or with meat.
Nice cold, but can be made warm quickly.
They make you strong and require no digestive strength to assimilate them.
Children like them as much as men.
Brain, body and muscle are all fed.

The dealer will return your money if Heinz Beans fail to please.

See that you get them. They are the best.

Large tin. 1/-
Smaller sizes, 6½d. & 9d.
At all Grocers and Stores

An advertisement for Heinz beans, 1900

## Questions

1 Do you think all the advertising claims are true? Which claims do you disagree with, and why?
2 Baked beans cost 5p a can in 1900. Why do you think a can of beans costs relatively less today, considering that we earn much more than people did in 1900?
3 Describe two of your favourite meals using baked beans.
4 Imagine that you lived in the 21st century. Design an advertisement for baked beans which might be used then.

## THE COMPOSITION OF MILK

| Type of milk | Energy kcal | Total fat g | Saturated fat g | Protein g | Carbo-hydrate g | Calcium mg | Riboflavin (Vit B₂) mg | Vitamin A μg | MILK KNOW-HOW |
|---|---|---|---|---|---|---|---|---|---|
| | | | | Content per pint | | | | | |
| Pasteurized whole milk | 380 | 22.2 | 13.2 | 19.3 | 27.5 | 702 | 1.11 | 228 | Pasteurized milk is heated to 72°C for at least 15 seconds. Then it is cooled to 4 – 5°C. This makes the milk safe to drink and helps it keep longer. |
| Pasteurized homogenized whole milk | 380 | 22.2 | 13.2 | 19.3 | 27.5 | 702 | 1.11 | 228 | The fat globules in homogenized milk have been broken up so that there is no cream on the top of the milk. |
| Pasteurized Channel Islands whole milk | 445 | 28.1 | 16.8 | 21.1 | 27.5 | 702 | 1.11 | 333 | Jersey and Guernsey cows produce Channel Islands milk which is very creamy and has more fat than other milk. |
| Pasteurized semi-skimmed milk | 280 | 10.5 | 6.3 | 19.5 | 28.4 | 729 | 1.12 | 104 | Some of the fat has been removed from semi-skimmed milk, so it has a lower energy value. It should not be given to babies and young children. |
| Pasteurized skimmed milk | 195 | 0.6 | 0.3 | 19.9 | 29.3 | 761 | 1.17 | Trace | Skimmed milk has almost all the fat removed. It doesn't have vitamins A and D, but it does have calcium, protein and other vitamins. It has a low energy value and is useful for slimmers. It should not be given to babies and young children. |
| Sterilized whole milk | 380 | 22.2 | 13.2 | 19.3 | 27.5 | 702 | 1.11 | 228 | This milk is heated and homogenized, then it is put into bottles and capped. The bottles are heated to 115 – 130°C for 10 – 30 minutes. This milk will keep for several months if it isn't opened. |
| UHT whole milk | 380 | 22.2 | 13.2 | 19.3 | 27.5 | 702 | 1.11 | 228 | Ultra heat treated (UHT) milk is homogenized and heated to at least 132°C for 1–2 seconds. It is packed into special cartons which protect it from light and oxygen. It will keep in a food cupboard for several months. |

Source: McCance and Widdowson's *The Composition of Foods*, 4th revised edition by A.A. Paul and D.A.T. Southgate (1978)

## Questions

Use the chart above, 'The composition of milk'.

1 Put the milks in order of their energy value (Kcal), starting with the highest value (Channel Islands).
2 Draw a bar chart like the one below. Draw a bar to show the total fat content of each milk.
3 Choose a suitable milk for each of the three people. Give your reasons.

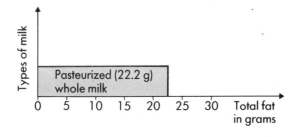

Total fat in milks

Michelle's daughter who likes milk with her breakfast

Mr Brown Who has a poor heart

Jenny who is over weight

## Quick quiz

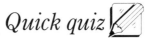

Use the chart above to answer these quick questions. Only write *one* sentence for each.

1 Why is milk pasteurized?
2 What is the difference between homogenized and pasteurized whole milk?
3 How does Channel Island milk get its name?
4 Which two milks are unsuitable for babies and young toddlers?
5 Why do you think people buy sterilized and UHT milk?

# Investigation

Find out which milk your class likes best.
Collect as many types of milk as you can find. If
possible, use dried milk and soya milk. Pour each
milk into a glass jug and chill in the fridge.

Work in groups and fill in the chart below.

| Milk | Appearance | Taste | Group Kevin's | |
|------|-----------|-------|------------------|------------------|
| | | | did you like it? | did you dislike it? |
| Channel Islands | Golden, with creamy top layer | Creamy and thick | ✓ ✓ ✓ | ✓ |

Find out which milk is the most popular with your
class. With the leftover milk treat yourselves to a
Strawberry whizz!

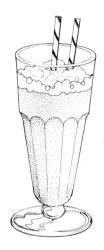

# Strawberry whizz

**Ingredients**
300 ml milk, 1 egg, a little sugar, 2 strawberries

**Method**
Put all the ingredients in a liquidizer or processor
and whizz until thick and foamy. Serve in tall
glasses.

# Milk wordsearch

Hidden in the puzzle are 19
words to do with milk and milky
foods. From the words you find
make a list of: (a) types of milk
(*six* altogether), (b) types of
cheese (*eleven* altogether), (C)
floaters (*two*).

| | | | | | | | | | | | | | | | |
|--|--|--|--|--|--|--|--|--|--|--|--|--|--|--|--|
| H | A | P | Q | J | S | M | O | K | E | D | Y | A | P | Y | P | P | R |
| I | S | K | I | M | M | E | D | V | P | C | H | E | D | D | A | R | X |
| C | T | P | L | R | L | P | V | J | T | C | F | L | P | X | S | V | E |
| T | I | J | C | P | Q | A | X | E | V | A | P | O | R | A | T | E | D |
| M | L | L | K | H | C | R | E | A | M | J | A | H | A | J | E | J | A |
| P | T | X | K | D | J | M | J | T | C | H | P | Q | J | F | U | F | M |
| C | O | T | T | A | G | E | Q | C | S | Y | O | G | H | U | R | T | X |
| L | N | V | C | L | Y | S | J | C | K | B | W | D | B | S | I | F | G |
| T | X | B | L | U | E | A | W | D | R | I | E | D | Q | Z | Z | O | O |
| V | C | U | R | D | X | N | J | T | Q | I | J | D | X | F | E | T | A |
| R | Q | T | V | Q | H | O | M | O | G | E | N | I | Z | E | D | X | T |
| C | V | T | J | C | X | Z | V | R | Q | W | J | T | D | K | M | Q | A |
| K | M | E | N | T | J | Y | C | O | N | D | E | N | S | E | D | Q | W |
| L | M | R | S | S | P | B | R | I | E | Z | Z | J | T | D | L | N | D |

**Answers**

*milk:* skimmed, evaporated,
condensed, dried.
pasteurized, homogenized,
*cheese:* cream,
Edam, Stilton, Blue,
Cheddar, cottage,
Parmesan, feta,
smoked, goat, Brie.
*floaters:* butter,
yoghurt.

## Investigation

Each group should choose an egg then follow the investigation:

1  Roll your egg gently on a large, flat surface. It should return to you. Perhaps nature's way of keeping an egg near to the nest?

2  Try spinning a raw egg. Impossible! The friction inside the egg makes it wobble. Hard-boiled eggs will spin, though.

3  Crack an egg onto a white plate. Look inside the shell. You will see the **membrane** which protects the inner egg. At the blunt end is an **air sac** which gets bigger as the egg becomes stale. Label your group's shell then arrange the shells in order of **air sac** size. Who has the freshest egg?

4  Compare all the cracked eggs. You should see three layers-
   • thin white
   • thick white
   • yolk.
   The egg with the highest yolk and thickest white is the freshest. Is this order the same as the shells?

5  Use a magnifying lens and look carefully at the egg. On the yolk is a white circle, the **germinal disc**, where the chick would develop. At the end of the yolk is a curly string, the **chalaza**, which holds the yolk in place. There may be a bloodspot, but this is harmless.

   You can now cook your egg.
   **Either** slide your egg gently into a saucepan of boiling water then watch it cook.
   **Or** beat the egg with a little milk, salt and pepper. Heat some margarine in a pan, pour in the egg mixture and cook and stir until the egg is scrambled.

   Now sit down and eat your experiment.

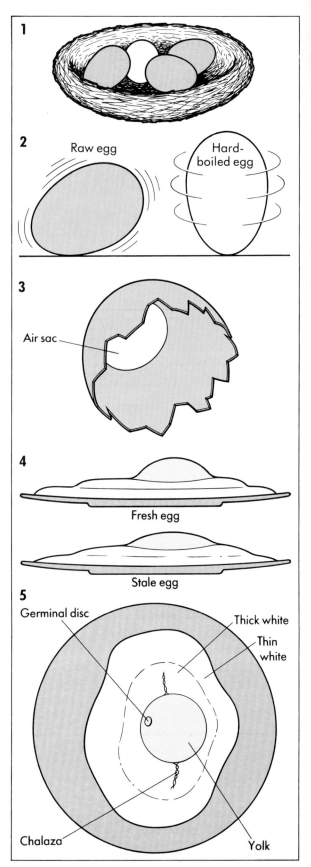

1

2  Raw egg    Hard-boiled egg

3  Air sac

4  Fresh egg

   Stale egg

5  Germinal disc    Thick white    Thin white

   Chalaza    Yolk

# Coloured and decorated Easter eggs

Since ancient times the egg has been a symbol of new life, and red coloured eggs were given at spring festivals to bring fertility and good fortune. The Christian church took the egg as a symbol of Easter and in many European countries eggs are dyed and decorated at Easter time. The first chocolate Easter eggs were made in France in the 19th century, and now nearly 100 million are sold each year in Britain.

Painted and decorated eggs from around the world

An egg provides all the food a chick needs before it is hatched. They are also an important cooking ingredient, especially for omelettes, cakes and pancake batters.

"delivered to store 48 hours after being laid. Average egg is composed of 11% shell, 58% white, 31% yolk."

An egg carton

### NUTRITION

Eggs are high in protein, which promotes strong healthy growth; rich in Vitamin $B_{12}$ for a healthy blood and nervous system, and Vitamin D for strong bones and teeth.
The protein is present almost equally in the white and yolk, while the vitamins are more abundant in the yolk.

|  | TYPICAL VALUES | |
| --- | --- | --- |
|  | PER 100g (3½ oz) | PER EGG |
| ENERGY | 145 K/CALORIES 610 K/JOULES | 80 K/CALORIES 340 K/JOULES |
| PROTEIN | 12.3g | 6.8g |
| CARBOHYDRATE | 0.4g | 0.2g |
| TOTAL FAT | 10.9g | 6.1g |
| of which POLYUNSATURATES | 1.8g | 1.0g |
| SATURATES | 3.0g | 1.7g |

| VITAMINS/MINERALS: % OF THE RECOMMENDED DAILY AMOUNT | | |
| --- | --- | --- |
| RIBOFLAVIN (VITAMIN $B_2$) | 30% | 15% |
| VITAMIN $B_{12}$ | 85% | 45% |
| VITAMIN D | 70% | 40% |
| IODINE | 35% | 20% |

## Questions

Use the label from the egg carton above to answer the questions.

1  When were these eggs packed and when should they be sold? How many days are allowed between packing and selling?
2  When do you think these eggs were laid?
3  How should eggs be stored?
4  What is the percentage composition of the three parts of the egg? You may need to refer to food tables.
5  Eggs provide us with valuable nutrients. Write about these nutrients and their importance in our diet.
6  Use the chart 'Typical values'. Add up the grams of protein, carbohydrate and total fat in 100 g egg. Take this total away from 100 g to find out roughly how much water there is in 100 g of egg.
100 g - (total amount of nutrients) = grams of water in 100 g of egg

7  Use the details from **6** to draw a bar chart like the one below:

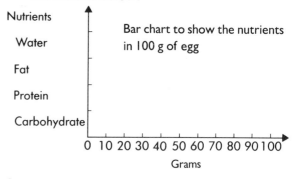

Bar chart to show the nutrients in 100 g of egg

8  A size 3 egg weighs about 60 g. How much does it cost?

### Answers

1 7 June, 20 June, 13 days;
2 5 June, 4 roughly 76% allowing for minerals and vitamins; 6 76.4 g

# Eggs for meals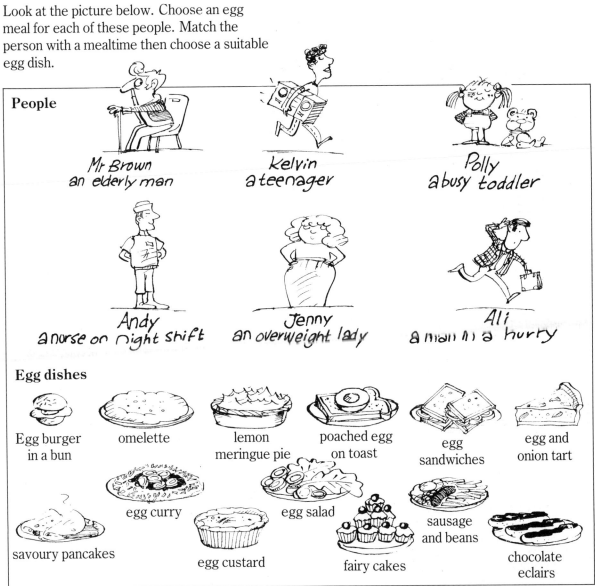

Look at the picture below. Choose an egg meal for each of these people. Match the person with a mealtime then choose a suitable egg dish.

**People**

Mr Brown
an elderly man

Kelvin
a teenager

Polly
a busy toddler

Andy
a nurse on night shift

Jenny
an overweight lady

Ali
a man in a hurry

**Egg dishes**

Egg burger in a bun

omelette

lemon meringue pie

poached egg on toast

egg sandwiches

egg and onion tart

egg curry

egg salad

savoury pancakes

egg custard

sausage and beans

fairy cakes

chocolate eclairs

What other foods could you serve with this meal?
Write a sentence about why you chose this meal.
Now copy and fill in the details on a chart like the one opposite.
An example has been filled in already.

| Person | Mealtime | Egg dish chosen and other food | Why this choice? |
|--------|----------|-------------------------------|------------------|
| Mr Brown | a snack | egg sandwiches, tomato, apple, cup of tea | Mr Brown is elderly and likes something easy to eat and easy to make, and he always drinks tea with every meal! |

73

## Investigation

What is the best way to whisk up an egg white?

Work in four groups.
**Each group needs:** an egg, a knife, two clean bowls, a tablespoon, a stopwatch or clock, a balloon whisk **or** electric whisk/processor **or** rotary whisk **or** fork.

Copy out the chart below and fill in the details as you work.

| Whisk used | Time taken to whisk egg stiffly | Tablespoons of unwhisked egg white | Flat tablespoons of whisked egg white |
|---|---|---|---|
| balloon whisk<br><br>rotary whisk<br><br>electric whisk or processor<br><br>fork | 2 minutes | 1 tablespoon | 4 tablespoons |

### Method

1. Separate the egg into yolk and white. One way is to crack the egg in half with a knife then let the white slip out, keeping the yolk in the shell.
   \*If you get yolk in your white go to step 5.
2. Put the white in a clean bowl, and measure the amount using a tablespoon.
3. Whisk the egg white until stiff. When you can turn the bowl upside down, it is ready. Write down how long this took. Measure the volume of egg white in level tablespoons.
4. Fill in the chart and compare your results with others.
5. Egg yolk in the white. Follow the experiment, exactly as if the mistake had never happened, from step 2. The yolky white takes longer to whisk up and the volume is less. You can mix this egg with orange juice or milk and honey to make a drink.

## To do

With your whisked egg whites and yolk you can make some **Floating Islands**.

| Ingredients | Equipment |
|---|---|
| 150 ml milk | bowl |
| a little sugar and | fork |
| vanilla essence | large frying pan |
| egg yolk | tablespoon |
| whisked white | plate |

### Method

1. Mix the milk, sugar and egg yolk in a bowl.
2. Heat this mixture gently in a frying pan.
3. Mix a little sugar and vanilla essence into the egg white, add 4 spoonfuls of egg white into the sauce, simmer for 2-3 minutes.
4. Serve the 'islands' hot with the egg sauce poured over the top.

Now answer the questions.

## Questions

1. What happens as the egg white is whisked?
2. What do you think is the best way to whisk an egg white, and why?
3. Which result produced the largest volume (the most whisked egg white)?
4. What problems did you have with this work?

A fish finger packet

## 10 FISH FINGERS
### FINEST FISH AVAILABLE TO YOU FROM TESCO

Value for money fish fingers cut from quality minced white fish and coated in a traditional breadcrumb. This economy priced product is ideal for all the family.

**COOKING INSTRUCTIONS:**
For best results always cook from frozen.

**TO SHALLOW FRY:**
Melt a little fat or oil in a frying pan over a medium heat and fry for about 6 minutes turning once.

**TO DEEP FRY:**
Lower into pan ⅓rd full of fat heated to 180°C/350°F and fry for 3-4 minutes.

**TO GRILL:**
Place on a grill pan under a medium heat for about 5 minutes turning once.

**SERVING SUGGESTION:**
Serve with crusty bread and salad.

**INGREDIENTS:**
White Fish, Breadcrumbs (with colours Turmeric, Annatto), Batter (Wheatflour, Water, Salt), Hydrogenated Vegetable Oil.

**TO STORE**
This product will keep for 12 hours if stored in a cool place, or for 3 days if stored unopened in the ice-making compartment of a refrigerator. If your refrigerator has a 'star' marked frozen food compartment, the maximum recommended storage times are:
★ 1 week ★★ 1 month ★★★ 3 months and for Food Freezers: ☆ ★★★ 3 months.
**IMPORTANT: DO NOT REFREEZE ONCE THAWED**

**TESCO QUALITY**
If you are not entirely satisfied with any Tesco product, please return it to the store where it was purchased, where we will be pleased to replace it. Or send it, with the packaging, to the Consumer Relations Manager, at the following address, stating where and when it was purchased. This offer does not affect your Statutory rights. Produced in the UK for Tesco Stores Ltd. P.O. BOX 18, Cheshunt, Herts., EN8 9SL. © Tesco 87    0268

| NUTRITION | | |
|---|---|---|
| | GRILLED | |
| AVERAGE COMPOSITION | PER 25g fish finger | PER 100g (3½ oz) |
| Energy | 198kJ/47kcal | 791kJ/189 kcal |
| Fat | 1.9g | 7.5g |
| Protein | 3.6g | 14.2g |
| Carbohydrate | 4.3g | 17g |
| Added Salt | 0.1g | 0.5g |
| INFORMATION | | |

## Questions

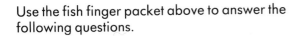

Use the fish finger packet above to answer the following questions.

1. What kinds of white fish might be used to make fish fingers?
2. How much does each fish finger weigh?
3. Copy the chart below and complete it for 'fish fingers'.
   Write a sentence to compare the difference in nutrients for each fish.

**Chart to show the composition of 100 g grilled cod and 100 g fish fingers**

| Type of fish | Protein | Fat | Carbohydrate |
|---|---|---|---|
| grilled cod | 21 g | 1.3 g | 0 g |
| fish fingers (grilled) | | | |

| NUTRITION | | |
|---|---|---|
| | GRILLED | |
| AVERAGE COMPOSITION | PER 25g fish finger | PER 100g (3½ oz) |
| Energy | 198kJ/47kcal | 791kJ/189 kcal |
| Fat | 1.9g | 7.5g |
| Protein | 3.6g | 14.2g |
| Carbohydrate | 4.3g | 17g |
| Added salt | 0.1g | 0.5g |
| INFORMATION | | |

4. 100 g grilled cod provides 420 KJ/100 Kcal. Why does a 100 g portion of fish fingers have a higher energy value (more kilojoules/kilocalories)?
5. How should these fish fingers be stored?
6. What is the healthiest way to cook fish fingers? Which method do you prefer and why?
7. Plan an evening meal, for yourself and two friends, which includes fish fingers.

Meat can be expensive and sometimes you buy a lot of bones, fat and skin which you do not want to eat.

## Investigation

Find out which meat is the best value for money.

Work in groups and look at 100 g portions of different cuts of meat. You can choose other cuts from the ones suggested on the chart below.

**Method**

1   Remove any bones, skin and fat from the meat and label this **waste**.
2   Weigh the waste and weigh the lean meat which is left. Check that the two add up to 100 g, then copy and complete the chart.
3   Simmer the meat in a little salted water for 30 minutes. Form a tasting panel and taste each meat. Write a sentence about each one.

| Name of cut meat | Cost per kilogram (1000 g) | Cost per 100 g (1 kg ÷ 10) | Weight of lean | Weight of waste | How much would 100 g of just lean meat cost? |
|---|---|---|---|---|---|
| Lamb chops | | | | | |
| Belly of pork | | | | | |
| Chicken leg | £2·20 | 22p | 60g | 40g | 36p |
| Stewing beef | | | | | |
| | | | | | |

**Tip**   Since the meat is usually sold in pounds and ounces, you need to work out the cost per kilogram.

If lamb chops cost £1.82 per pound

Then one kilogram costs      cost per pound      x      number of pounds in a kilogram

£1.82                                        2.2                                              = £4.00

How can you work out how much it would cost if you bought 100 g of just lean meat?

*These sums are hard!*

If 100 g chicken leg portion cost 22p, with 60 g lean and 40 g waste (bone, skin, fat) how much would 100 g just lean meat cost?

60 g lean meat cost 22p
1 g lean meat cost 22 ÷ 60p
100 g lean meat costs 100 × 22p ÷ 60  = 36p

*I can do that!*

# Questions

1  Draw bar charts like the ones below to show:
   (a) the different amounts of waste for each meat,
   (b) the cost of 100 g lean meat.

2  Which meat did you think was the best value for money? **Remember** that tough cuts such as stewing beef need longer cooking, and this adds to their cost.

3  For each cut of meat find two recipes which you would enjoy cooking.

(a) Bar chart to show the amount of waste from different meats

Meat

Chicken 40 g

0   10   20   30   40   50   60
Waste in grams

(b) Bar chart to show the cost for 100 g lean meat

Meat

Chicken 36p

0   10p   20p   30p   40p   50p   60p
cost for 100 g lean meat

# To do

Meat is used in many famous dishes throughout the world. Copy and complete the diagram. Match up the meats with their recipes and the country or region which the recipe may have come from. Add ideas of your own.

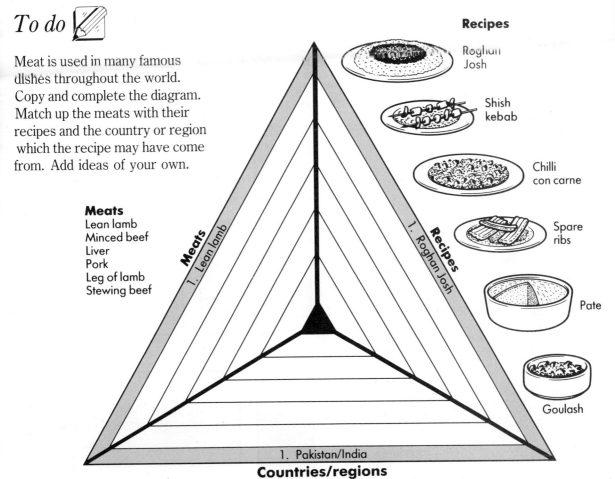

**Recipes**

Roghan Josh

Shish kebab

Chilli con carne

Spare ribs

Pate

Goulash

**Meats**
Lean lamb
Minced beef
Liver
Pork
Leg of lamb
Stewing beef

**Meats**
1. Lean lamb

**Recipes**
1. Roghan Josh

1. Pakistan/India

**Countries/regions**

**Countries**  Pakistan/India, China, Mexico/Texas, Middle East, Hungary, France

77

A kitchen should be safe and easy to use as it is a busy place. If possible, work out the layout of a kitchen before spending money on new equipment and kitchen furniture.

## To do

Design your own kitchen.

1 Copy out the scaled drawing of the kitchen onto squared paper.
2 On a separate sheet, draw to scale the kitchen equipment and furniture items. You may need more 'single kitchen units', 'double units' and 'stools' and 'chairs'.
3 Cut out the pieces you think you will use. Add some more ideas of your own.
4 Move the paper pieces around your kitchen plan until you get the best fit. Stick the pieces onto the paper.
5 Draw in:
    (a) the positions of the electric sockets,
    (b) a gas point if used,
    (c) the water supply.

## Tips

● Make sure the cooker, sink and refrigerator are not too far apart.
● Put a work surface beside the cooker so that hot dishes can be placed down safely.
● Keep the cooker away from opening doors and windows.
● Place electric switches away from water sources.

Cooker

Hob

Tumble drier

Upright freezer

Refrigerator

Sink unit

Dishwasher

Single kitchen unit

Double kitchen unit

Stool

Chair

Electric socket

Water supply

Gas point

Tall cupboard

Rubbish bin

Half unit or cupboard

Sink unit

Kitchen units

Scale: 10 squares = 1 metre

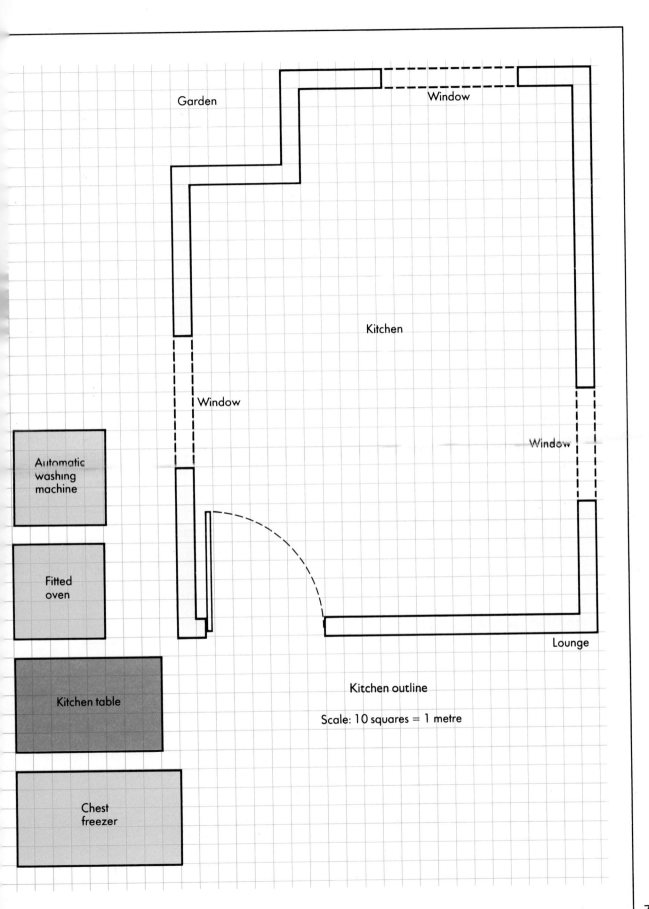

Garden

Window

Kitchen

Window

Window

Lounge

Automatic
washing
machine

Fitted
oven

Kitchen table

Chest
freezer

Kitchen outline

Scale: 10 squares = 1 metre

## To do

Imagine that you are making a cup of tea in your kitchen. Draw a line on your plan for each of these journeys, and write the number of each journey on the line like in the diagram below.

**Making a cup of tea**
1   Collect the kettle (where is it kept?).
2   Fill the kettle with water.
3   Put the kettle on to boil (you may plug it in or boil it on the cooker).
4   Collect tea cup, saucer, teaspoon.
5   Collect tea bags and sugar.
6   Place tea bag in cup.
7   Fetch milk from refrigerator.
8   Pour boiling water over tea bag.
9   Remove tea bag and place in rubbish bin.
10   Add milk and sugar if used.
11   Sit down and drink your tea!

Now look carefully at your plan. Should you move any things to make the journeys easier? Draw a sketch of your new design. If you liked your first design, why do you think the layout worked so well?

## Questions

1   On squared paper draw *your own* kitchen to scale. Use a scale of 10 squares to 1 metre. Mark in the position of all units and large equipment. Imagine that you are making a cup of tea in this kitchen. Draw in your journeys. How well planned is your kitchen?
2   Collect pictures and leaflets about kitchen units and equipment from magazines, newspapers and shops. Design a huge poster and stick in your pictures. Give it the title 'Kitchen planning'.
3   Imagine that you lived in the year 2100. What sort of kitchen might you use? Draw a picture of your ideas. **Remember**, perhaps we might not do so much cooking then!

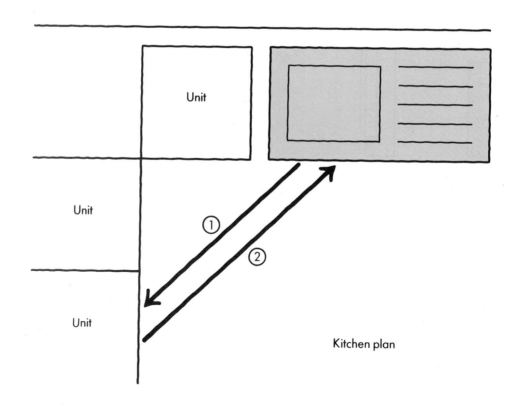

Kitchen plan

# Why are we using more electrical equipment?

More and more people are using electrical equipment in the home. Most people have a cooker or microwave. Look at the charts below. They show the changes in the percentage of people using certain pieces of equipment.

1 Mr and Mrs Supercook use most of these pieces of equipment. Are they different from most families? Use the bar charts to help you with your answers.

2 Which pieces of equipment have become more popular over the years? Why do you think this is?

3 Look at the figures for 1984. What percentage of homes do not have a refrigerator or a washing machine? How do they manage to:
(a) keep food cool,
(b) do their washing without a washing machine?

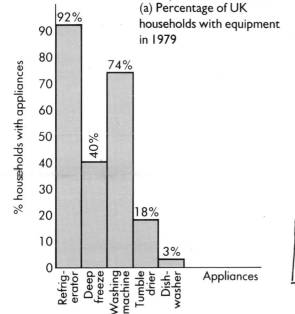

(a) Percentage of UK households with equipment in 1979

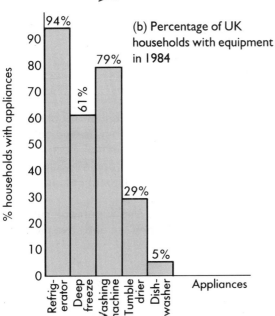

(b) Percentage of UK households with equipment in 1984

## Percentages

A **percentage** is 'out of a hundred'.

**Question**  If 5 per cent (%) of households have a dishwasher, how many don't?
5 out of 100 have a dishwasher.
Number who don't = 100 − 5 = 95, so 95% don't have a dishwasher.

When food is sold to us it is often weighed out in kilograms or pounds. Electricity is sold by the **unit**. One unit of electricity is used at the rate of one kilowatt (1 kw) or 1000 watts for one hour. So for one unit, a one kilowatt electric fire will give off heat for one hour.

## To do

Mr and Mrs Supercook and their two children use the electrical equipment in their kitchen shown in the table opposite. Work out how many units of electricity they use each week.

*I can't do this!*

| Equipment | Units of electricity a week |
|---|---|
| cooker – one week's meals for the family uses 17 units | 17 units |
| fridge freezer – running for 7 days (uses 2 units a day) | |
| kettle – boils 49 litres water (7 litres boiled used 1 unit) | |
| iron – 6 hours per week (2 hours used 1 unit) | |
| washing machine – 2 loads washing (1 load uses 5 units) | |
| tumble drier – 2 loads (1 load used 2 units) | |
| dishwasher – 14 loads (1 load uses 2 units) | |
| electric fire – 21 hours (1 hour uses 1 unit) | |
| microwave – 1 hour 40 minutes for 1 unit | 1 unit |
| *Total* | units |

## Dishwasher

If 1 load uses 2 units then 14 loads uses 14 x 2 = 28 units

*Now I can work out the rest!*

## Questions

1 Look at your electricity bill or ask at the local electricity showrooms to find out how much you pay for each unit of electricity.
2 Work out how much Mr and Mrs Supercook have to pay each week for the equipment above.
3 How could Mr and Mrs Supercook cut down on the electricity they use and save money?

**Answer:** number of units = 105.

# £1500 to spend on your kitchen!

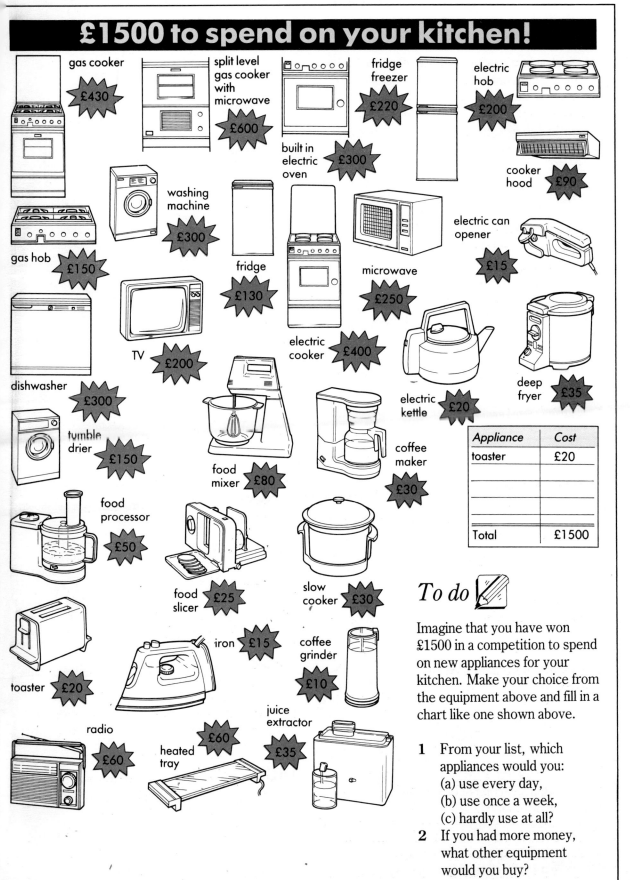

gas cooker **£430**

split level gas cooker with microwave **£600**

fridge freezer **£220**

electric hob **£200**

built in electric oven **£300**

cooker hood **£90**

washing machine **£300**

gas hob **£150**

fridge **£130**

microwave **£250**

electric can opener **£15**

TV **£200**

electric cooker **£400**

electric kettle **£20**

deep fryer **£35**

dishwasher **£300**

tumble drier **£150**

food mixer **£80**

coffee maker **£30**

food processor **£50**

food slicer **£25**

slow cooker **£30**

iron **£15**

coffee grinder **£10**

toaster **£20**

radio **£60**

heated tray **£60**

juice extractor **£35**

| Appliance | Cost |
|---|---|
| toaster | £20 |
|  |  |
|  |  |
|  |  |
| Total | £1500 |

## To do

Imagine that you have won £1500 in a competition to spend on new appliances for your kitchen. Make your choice from the equipment above and fill in a chart like one shown above.

1  From your list, which appliances would you:
   (a) use every day,
   (b) use once a week,
   (c) hardly use at all?
2  If you had more money, what other equipment would you buy?

83

An electric kettle is just a kettle fitted with a heating element and a connecting cord to mains electricity.

Aluminium kettles are often the cheapest but the metal dents and scratches easily.

Stainless steel kettles are strong and difficult to dent or scratch.

Plastic kettles are strong and difficult to dent or chip. If you leave them near a hot plate they can melt!

Enamelled steel kettles are quite tough and don't dent easily, but enamel chips.

Chrome plated kettles often cover copper which dents easily.

Copper kettles are often sealed to stop the copper becoming dull. They are not popular.

What are kettles made from?

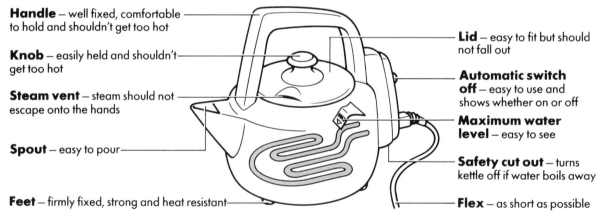

**Handle** – well fixed, comfortable to hold and shouldn't get too hot

**Knob** – easily held and shouldn't get too hot

**Steam vent** – steam should not escape onto the hands

**Spout** – easy to pour

**Feet** – firmly fixed, strong and heat resistant

**Lid** – easy to fit but should not fall out

**Automatic switch off** – easy to use and shows whether on or off

**Maximum water level** – easy to see

**Safety cut out** – turns kettle off if water boils away

**Flex** – as short as possible

What makes a good kettle?

## To do

### How good is your kettle?

**You need:** a selection of electric kettles, a stopwatch or timer.

Work in small groups. Each group has one kettle. At the end of the investigation each group must tell the rest of the class about their findings.

### Method

1 Draw and label your kettle. Use the drawing above to help.
2 Write down any details printed on the kettle and find out roughly how much it cost.
3 What is the kettle made from?

4　Now fill the kettle with water. Time how long it takes to boil. Now answer these questions.
(a) How is the kettle filled?
(b) How much water did you use and what made you decide on this amount?
(c) How long did the water take to boil?
(d) What happened to the kettle when the water began to boil?
(e) What do you think is the **capacity** of the kettle – the amount needed to fill it up?

5　Compare the boiling time of your kettle with others. To do this fill each kettle with one litre of cold water, bring to the boil and write down the time this took. Draw a chart of the results. Why do you think the kettles took different times to boil?

## Questions

1　Draw two kettles, one safe, one dangerous. Label the safe and dangerous parts.
2　How would you choose an electric kettle for:
(a) an elderly lady,
(b) a mother with young children?
3　Collect details of different electric kettles from shops, newspapers, and magazines. Which kettle would you choose for yourself and why?

### Electric kettles are dangerous!

Boiling water and steam from kettles can scald, and young children can easily pull the kettle flex. Kettles should be well designed and used carefully. In Birmingham Accident Hospital Burns Unit, 250 burns victims are treated each year. Over 20 of them have been scalded by electric kettles. This means that more than 1000 serious kettle scalds probably happen in the UK every year.

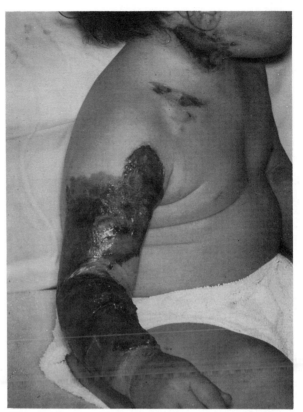

This child was scalded by water from a kettle (RoSPA)

# First aid for scalds

**ACT QUICKLY** – the longer you delay, the deeper the burn will go. A delay in cooling a burn increases the depth of the burn. Cool the burnt area in plenty of cold water. You can put young children in a bath of cold water.

People can die from scalds. Serious scalds need medical help, so ring for the doctor or dial 999 and ask for the ambulance service. Go back to the victim and stay with them until help arrives.

## Further work

Most people have been scalded, if only slightly, at some time. Write about when and how this happened to you. (If it hasn't then ask a friend or invent a story.) How could the accident have been avoided? What first aid treatment was given?

Why do we need to weigh and measure things? One reason is to follow recipes. When people invent a special dish, others like to copy it for themselves, so they use their recipe. Sometimes this is not so easy, because recipes can be muddled.

Look at this old recipe for rice pudding. Even the picture showing rice is wrong.

Rice Pudding.

*Ingredients.*—1 quart milk, skim or new, a breakfastcupful of rice, not quite a teaspoonful of sugar, a few drops of the "Standard" flavouring essences, either Ratafia, or Vanilla, or a grate of nutmeg.
  *How to use them.*—Put the milk into a large pie-dish with the rice, sugar, and flavouring, and give a stir. Set the dish on the stove to soak (the longer the better), then put it in the oven, and bake till the rice is thoroughly done.

Cost, with new milk, *5d.*, for pudding for 6 children.

Ears of Rice.

**Recipe for rice pudding**

How much milk, rice and sugar do you think this recipe uses?

Food needs to be weighed to find out how heavy it is.

There are several sorts of scales used for weighing food:

# Scales

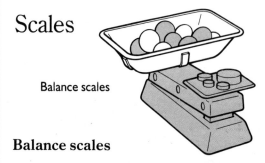

Balance scales

**Balance scales**

Food is put in one scale pan and little brass or iron weights in the other. Before starting, check that with two empty pans, the balance is level. When the food and little weights weigh the same, the balance is level once more.

**Spring balance scales**

Before you weigh anything on these scales, make sure the pointer on the number face is at zero when the scale pan is in place. Then simply measure the food until the pointer reaches the weight you need.

Spring balance scales

**Electronic scales**

These are expensive to buy but simple to use. Simply measure the food into the scale pan and watch the digits record the weight.

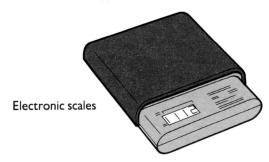

Electronic scales

# Guess the weight

If you want to use food tables to find the nutrients in food, it is useful to know how much an apple, for example, weighs.

*To do*

Work in groups. Copy and complete the chart at the top of the next page. Guess, then weigh, each of the foods listed. Give yourselves a mark if you guessed within 10 grams of the final weight. Add up your score.

| Food | Guessed weight | Real weight | Score |
|------|---------------|-------------|-------|
| 1 apple | | | |
| 1 large potato | | | |
| 1 size 3 egg | | | |
| 1 coffee cup full of sugar | | | |
| 1 coffee cup full of rice | | | |
| 1 level tablespoon flour | | | |
| 1 heaped tablespoon flour | | | |
| 1 large slice bread | | | |
| 1 bowl breakfast cereal | | | |
| Total score | | | |

# Liquid measures

The capacity or volume is the liquid measurement. This can be measured in ml = millilitres, 1 = litres, pt = pints.

Always stand the measuring jug on a level surface

Read off the measurements at eye level

# Solid measures

Mass or solid weights are measured in g = grams, kg = kilograms, oz = ounces, lb = pounds.

What is the difference between a level and heaped tablespoon?

**Level** tablespoon — level off with a knife

**Heaped** — the same amount in the spoon as on top

Most packaged food comes in 'standard' sizes. That is, the same size can may be used to pack fruits and vegetables. Fats such as butter or margarine are sold in similar weights.

# Questions

1  Find out in what sizes the following foods are sold:
   butter, flour, canned beans, canned drinks, sugar, bottled squash, coffee.
   Write down:
   (a) the **imperial measure**, the old system using pounds (lb), ounces (oz), pints, fluid ounces (fl. oz)
   (b) the metric measure using kilograms (kg), grams (g), litres (l), millilitres (ml).

2  Either visit your greengrocer or supermarket or weigh these foods to find the answers.
   (a) How many medium sized:
   ● apples
   ● bananas
   ● potatoes would you get in 1 kilogram (2.2lb)?
   (b) How much does
   ● a cabbage
   ● a tomato
   ● a carrot weigh?

# Hygiene in the kitchen

Rule

**1** Always wash your hands after using the toilet.

**2** Don't sneeze or cough on food. Use paper tissues to blow your nose on, throw them away and wash your hands afterwards.

**3** Don't lick food or dip your fingers into it. Use a clean spoon to taste food.

**4** Remove fancy rings and bangles before cooking. Cover cuts with a waterproof dressing.

**5** Cover clothes with a clean apron or overall before working in food areas.

**6** Don't brush your hair in the kitchen, and tie back long hair.

**7** Prepare food on clean work surface using clean utensils. Throw away chipped and cracked crockery.

**8** Keep pets and pet food out of the kitchen.

**9** Keep food covered and cool.

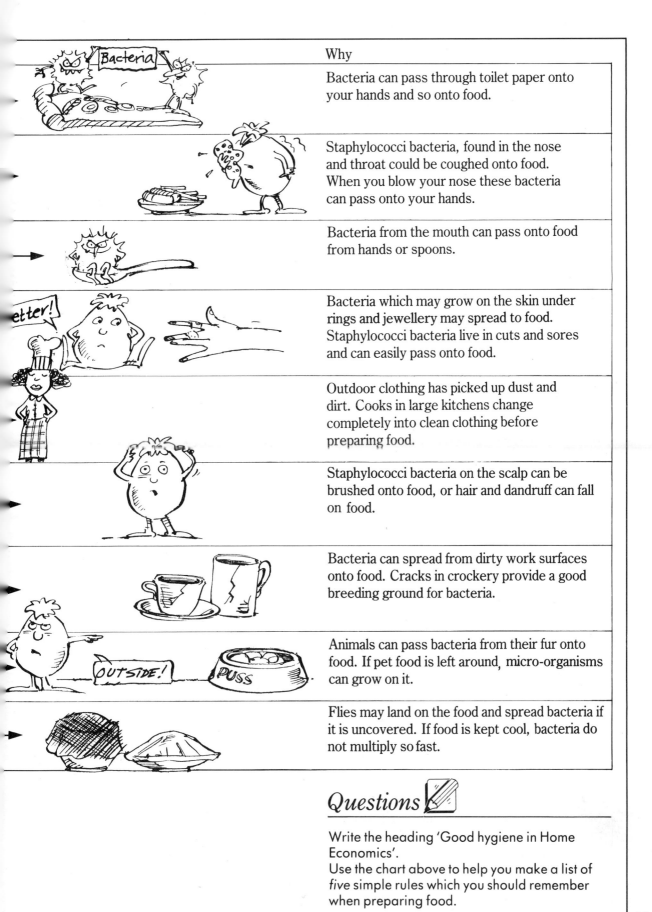

| | **Why** |
|---|---|
| | Bacteria can pass through toilet paper onto your hands and so onto food. |
| | Staphylococci bacteria, found in the nose and throat could be coughed onto food. When you blow your nose these bacteria can pass onto your hands. |
| | Bacteria from the mouth can pass onto food from hands or spoons. |
| | Bacteria which may grow on the skin under rings and jewellery may spread to food. Staphylococci bacteria live in cuts and sores and can easily pass onto food. |
| | Outdoor clothing has picked up dust and dirt. Cooks in large kitchens change completely into clean clothing before preparing food. |
| | Staphylococci bacteria on the scalp can be brushed onto food, or hair and dandruff can fall on food. |
| | Bacteria can spread from dirty work surfaces onto food. Cracks in crockery provide a good breeding ground for bacteria. |
| | Animals can pass bacteria from their fur onto food. If pet food is left around, micro-organisms can grow on it. |
| | Flies may land on the food and spread bacteria if it is uncovered. If food is kept cool, bacteria do not multiply so fast. |

## Questions

Write the heading 'Good hygiene in Home Economics'.

Use the chart above to help you make a list of *five* simple rules which you should remember when preparing food.

Bacteria are tiny one-celled organisms which can only be seen through a microscope. Bacteria are found all around us, and most of them are useful and important to our lives. Some bacteria, however, cause **food poisoning. If they are eaten they can make you ill. Vomiting, diarrhoea** and **tummy pains** are all symptoms of food poisoning.

To grow and breed, bacteria need four things: warmth, food, liquid and time.

It's getting too hot!

What a lovely warmth let's breed.

Brr... it's cold let's sleep.

## Warmth

The temperature bacteria like best is 37°C, the same as the human body. If it gets hotter, the growth of bacteria slows down and above 63°C bacteria begin to die. In boiling water they are usually killed in 1-2 minutes.

In cold temperatures, bacteria slow down but are not killed. Food poisoning bacteria will not grow in most refrigerators and are dormant or sleepy in frozen food. However, once the food warms up, bacteria begin to breed again.

## Foods

Bacteria like foods which are high in protein and contain water.

gravy

chicken

pies

sausages

burgers

ice cream

## Liquid

Bacteria need liquid to grow and breed. Dried foods such as dried potato, soup mix and milk powder do not contain enough water for bacteria to grow. But once you add the water, then they begin to breed.

## Time

Bacteria can divide in two every 20 minutes, as long as they have food, liquid and warmth. So after 20 minutes, one bacterium becomes two.

## To do

Copy the chart below and fill in the spaces to show how quickly bacteria multiply.

| Time in minutes | 0 | 20 | 40 | 60 | 80 | 100 | 120 |
|---|---|---|---|---|---|---|---|
| Number of bacteria | 1 | 2 | | 8 | | 32 | |

By reading the figures from the chart you can draw up a graph like the one on the right. The line across the page (the **horizontal** axis) represents the time in minutes. The line running up the page represents the number of bacteria. For each time, look up the number of bacteria. Copy the graph and mark with a cross (x) the point where the time and number of bacteria meet. The first three crosses have been completed. Join up the crosses with one line.

**Tip**  This line is not straight.

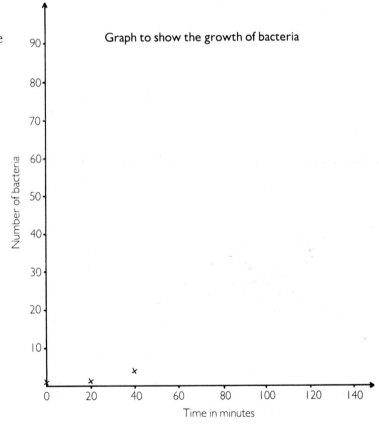

Graph to show the growth of bacteria

## Questions

1  What would happen if the bacteria were left to breed happily for one day?
2  How would you draw this result on a graph and what would be the problems?

## Quick quiz

1  What *four* things do bacteria need to grow?
2  What temperature do bacteria like best?
3  How could you kill bacteria?
4  What happens to bacteria when food is frozen?
5  Which foods do bacteria like: (a) least, (b) most?

# Hospital food poisoning spread by beef left out on warm day

### From Craig Seton, Wakefield

Cooked beef taken from a refrigerator and left for 10 hours in a kitchen and a ward on a warm day was responsible for the spread of the salmonella outbreak at the Stanley Royd psychiatric hospital in Wakefield, but the source of the original infection is still unknown.

The number of deaths reported since the food poisoning outbreak remained yesterday at 26, although laboratory tests on samples from 17 dead patients showed only 10 proved positive for salmonella infection.

No new suspected cases were officially reported yesterday. The number of patients suffering salmonella-type symptoms was 14—eight fewer than on Sunday—although seven are still seriously ill.

Officials refused yesterday to comment on a new report that four suspected cases of food poisoning are now being treated at the neighbouring Pinderfields Hospital. They said any comment would be made today.

The report suggested that three of the four patients at Pinderfields were from Stanley Royd.

Officials denied claims that conditions in the Stanley Royd hospital kitchens were unhygienic, but health service unions renewed calls for a full inquiry into the outbreak and criticized the Wakefield Health Authority's handling of it.

The news that roast beef prepared for a salad tea at the 900-bed Stanley Royd hospital on August 25 was "the vehicle by which the infection was spread" was given by Dr Geoffrey Ireland, district medical officer of the authority. But he told a press conference: "We are at a loss as to how it was introduced to the hospital kitchen."

Health officials believe the poisoning could have been introduced through raw meat, offal, poultry or eggs. The health authority said kitchen staff had been checked and those who had positive laboratory specimens sent home, but officials would not say how many had proved positive.

Dr Ireland said the beef had been cooked on August 24 and left in a refrigerator. At 7.15 am the following day it was taken out, sliced and left on trays ready for the 5 pm tea, leaving the kitchen between 2 pm and 3 pm.

He said: "The fact that it remained at the kitchen and ward temperature on a warm day for some 10 hours is significant; we firmly believe it allowed the organism to develop.

He said that while experts were still striving to find the source of the infection, in 60 per cent or 70 per cent of food poisoning cases the source was never found.

He added: "I believe that the beef should not really have left the refrigerator until after lunch - say between 1pm and 2pm. The fact that it was a warm day added to the problem. Why it came out at 7.15 in the morning must be looked into."

Hospital food poisoning (*The Times*)

# Questions

Use the newspaper article above, 'Hospital food poisoning', to answer the questions:

1  How many patients died from the outbreak of salmonella food poisoning and how many others were still ill?

2  Why did this outbreak of food poisoning happen?

3  Draw up a timeplan to show how the beef salad was prepared:
   August 24: beef was cooked and left in refrigerator
   August 25, 7.15 a.m. ...

4  What advice did Dr Ireland, the district medical officer, give on how to prepare the beef salad safely?

5  What do you think the following phrases mean?
   (a) 'the source of the original infection is still unknown'
   (b) 'the vehicle by which the infection was spread'
   (c) 'positive laboratory specimens'

These rules were given to a servant employed over a hundred years ago:

"Do not claw back your head or your back as if you are after a flea, or stroke your hair as if you sought a louse.

Do not pick your nose or let it drop clear pearls, or sniff or blow too hard, lest your lord hear.

Do not have the habit of squirting or sprouting with your mouth or gape or yawn or pout. And do not lick a dish with tongue to get out dust.

Do not sigh or cough or belch. Good son, do not pick your teeth or with puffing and blowing cast foul breath upon your lord."

Quite a servant!

## To do

Can you write four rules in simple language for this servant? For example:
**Rule 1**   Do not spit or lick the food.

## Questions

1   Write the heading 'Ten rules for the kitchen', and make up ten rules of your own to use when preparing food at home.
2   Design a poster which shows a picture of one of your rules for the kitchen.

The chart opposite shows ten-point codes given to people working in the food trade today. Jobs include working in restaurants, supermarkets, kitchens and factories.

## 10 POINT CODES FOR FOOD TRADE WORKERS

**1**   Wash your hands always before touching food, always after using the WC

**2**   Tell your supervisor at once of any skin, nose, throat or bowel trouble.

**3**   Cover cuts and sores with waterproof dressings.

**4**   Wear clean clothing and be clean.

**5**   Remember smoking in a food room is illegal and dangerous. Never cough or sneeze over food.

**6**   Clean as you go in food rooms.

**7**   Keep food clean, covered and either cool or piping hot.

**8**   Keep your hands off food as far as possible. Keep food utensils clean.

**9**   Keep the lid on the dustbin.

**10**   Remember the law requires clean, fully equipped, well lit and airy conditions for food preparation.

(Health Education Authority)

Answer the questions in each section then add up
the score and see the results.

## Fatty foods

**1** How often do you eat chips?
| very rarely or never | 0 |
| once a week | 2 |
| as often as possible | 3 |

**2** How often do you eat chocolates, crisps or
packets of nuts?
| very rarely | 0 |
| once or twice a week | 2 |
| as often as possible | 3 |

**3** When you cook hamburgers, sausages or
fish fingers, do you
| grill them | 1 |
| fry them | 3 |
| never eat them at all! | 0 |

**4** Which milk do you prefer?
| semi skimmed milk | 1 |
| full cream milk | 2 |
| neither | 1 |

**5** How often do you have a 'fry up' meal with
lots of fried food?
| very rarely or never | 0 |
| once a week | 2 |
| every day | 3 |

**Total score for fatty foods**          11

## Filler foods

**1** Do you eat breakfast cereal?
| every day | 4 |
| 3-5 days a week | 3 |
| 1-2 days a week | 2 |
| rarely or never | 0 |

**2** How often do you eat bread?
| twice a day | 4 |
| once a day | 3 |
| 2-3 times a week | 2 |

**3** How often do you eat rice, pasta or
potatoes?
| more than once a day | 3 |
| once a day | 2 |
| 2-3 times a week | 1 |
| once a week | 0 |

**4** How often do you eat root vegetables such
as swedes, sweet potatoes, parsnips or
yams?
| once or twice a week | 3 |
| once or twice a month | 1 |
| as little as possible | 0 |

**Total score for fillers**

How did you score?
If your score for **fatty foods** was lower than
your score for **filler foods** then you are probably
eating a sensible diet and should explain your
ideas to others.
If your score for **fatty foods** was higher than
your score for **filler foods** then you need to
watch what you eat. Where you scored high
marks in the **fatty foods** section shows types of
food you should cut down.
If the two scores were about the same then you
need to cut down on some fatty foods or eat
more filler foods.

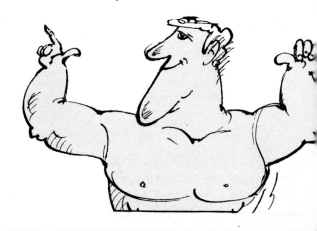

How well did I work?
After each piece of work, fill in a chart like the one opposite about yourself. Award yourself a mark out of 10 for each section, then answer *three* questions underneath.

## Sections

**a** I shared ideas and answers with others.
**b** I added my own ideas to the lesson.
**c** I explained things to others.
**d** I finished all the work.
**e** I did my best.
**f** I understood all the work.
**g** I enjoyed the work.

## Questions

**1** What was the most interesting thing you learned?
**2** What was the most boring part?
**3** How could your work improve?

How did you score?

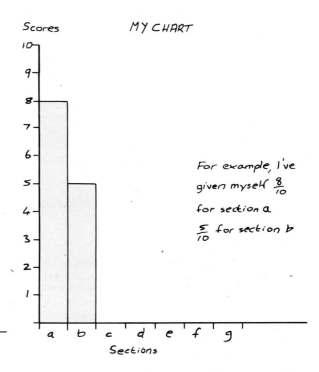

Scores    MY CHART

For example, I've given myself $\frac{8}{10}$ for section a $\frac{5}{10}$ for section b

Sections

most marks over 7

most marks below 5

most marks just over 5

# Index